Paul, Son of Kish

THE UNIVERSITY OF CHICAGO PRESS
CHICAGO, ILLINOIS

THE BAKER AND TAYLOR COMPANY
NEW YORK

THE CAMBRIDGE UNIVERSITY PRESS
LONDON

THE MARUZEN-KABUSHIKI-KAISHA
TOKYO, OSAKA, KYOTO, FUKUOKA, SENDAI

THE MISSION BOOK COMPANY
SHANGHAI

THE VICTOR

(See page 55)

Paul, Son of Kish

By
LYMAN I. HENRY

THE UNIVERSITY OF CHICAGO PRESS
CHICAGO ILLINOIS

Composed and Printed By
The University of Chicago Press
Chicago, Illinois, U.S.A.

To My Son

EDITORS' PREFACE

This book is itself a constructive study. Unlike other volumes in the series it has performed the constructive work instead of guiding the student in doing it for himself: the result is a complete story to be read and enjoyed.

It may be used in Bible classes in one of two ways:

In connection with any course of study in the life of Paul it may serve as collateral reading. There is great value in having a vivid story into which all the material of study may be fitted, and through which a unity of impression may be secured.

Or it may stimulate a group in a genuinely constructive task. It is confessedly a work of imagination founded on the facts. Let the students themselves seek the facts and decide whether they agree with the author in his interpretation of Paul's life and character. For example, each member of the class may examine a certain amount of the biblical material to discover what it contributes to a knowledge of Paul's youth. They may then compare this with the vivid treatment of the author, and form their own judgment of the probable reality.

THE EDITORS

FOREWORD

The experiences, sacrifices, and achievements of Paul, if appreciated by us, create a desire for more intimate knowledge of his preparation and equipment.

In this story the life of Saul of Tarsus, historically reconstructed, has been harmoniously blended by the use of fiction with the accounts of his life given in the New Testament.

In matters of customs, manners, and conditions, as well as in the use of important dates, the generally recognized historical authorities have been faithfully followed to aid in giving correct impressions.

Imagination, within historical bounds and probability, has supplied the restoration in the early part of Saul's life, and in the interims between later events. Interpretations of vital Scriptures by recognized scholars have not been violated, nor have recorded events been taken out of their settings. Events in Paul's life have been selected for continuity of the story, not for historical exegesis.

The admonition of Paul and Barnabas to the citizens of Lystra, "We also are men of like passions with you," has been the textual authority for presenting Paul humanized—the wholesome, courageous, and lovable man. Not only is he a man's man but also, by analogy, he is a boy's boy. In his time he spoke in terms understood by both young and old. His life, reproduced in his environment, interests the student of development and the admirer of his achievements.

Scenes and characters have been supplied by invention in an effort to realize, in narrative form, the vivid personality of Paul. His marriage to Tabitha qualifies him to become a member of the Sanhedrin; the adaptation of the legend of Thekla gives the customs and religion of the East, and the effect of his teachings; David, as a younger brother, supplies the necessary funds until the loyal brothers of Macedonia send relief to Rome; and Alexander, the coppersmith, as the wandering Jew, personifies the opposition to Paul. These and similar liberties, easily recognized as inventions, are merely aids in the visualization of the dramatic and interesting incidents in Paul's life.

It is impossible to make specific acknowledgment of the many able writers on the life and letters of Paul whose books have been helpful and influential in the composition of this story.

To Dr. Shirley J. Case, Professor of Early Church History and New Testament Interpretation in the University of Chicago, I am so deeply indebted that the expression of my sincere thanks to him in no sense discharges my obligation. With his scrupulous fidelity to historical accuracy and with his thorough knowledge of the period and events at the foundation of this story, he has advised and criticized generously and sympathetically to the end that, in this freedom of romantic reconstruction, no erroneous use of known facts and incidents would be permitted. In appreciation of his generous labors changes have been made to conform to his learned suggestions.

Paul the man! Irresistible! Incomparable!

His preparedness; the intensity of his life; his unswerving devotion to Jesus; his incalculable influence through the centuries to our day; the depths of his mysticism; his strong personality creating loyal friendships and exciting bitter animosities; his fearlessness, integrity, loyalty, and zeal; his keen sense of justice; his sweet reasonableness; and his exalted spirituality have inspired and will inspire unnumbered generations of men.

To visualize Paul and his heroically sacrificial life in terms of human experience as "a man of like passions with us," thoroughly equipped, has been the impelling motive in writing this story.

LYMAN I. HENRY

CONTENTS

PART V. MEDITATION AND PREPARATION

PART VI. HERALD, LEADER, MARTYR

ILLUSTRATIONS

By Louis Grell

xv

PART I

A Youth in Tarsus

CHAPTER I

SCHOOLS AND TENT-MAKING

The deep-water wharf in ancient Tarsus was teeming with activity. An Alexandrian grain ship being unloaded would receive a returning cargo. Freight was being assembled for another ship that was discharging military stores and soldiers from Rome. Bundles of spices, of dried fruits and of rare loom fabrics were being unslung from the pack trains of camels and donkeys while the swarthy owners from the East opened the packages to display their property for sale and barter. Merchants from Alexandria and from Rome in great excitement carried on loud and passionate arguments with the voluble men of the desert who were schooled in bargaining.

Two boys, about fifteen years of age, wandering aimlessly along the cluttered wharf, were closely watched by the desert-tanned owners of the merchandise lest curiosity might develop into appropriation. One of the lads, restless and undersized, was dressed in the blue-bordered, white garment affected by the Pharisees, while the other wore the somber robe of a Sadducee.

They stopped in front of a large, good-natured, Roman soldier who was busy at the moment in directing other soldiers to gather the luggage and equipment of the military company for a long journey across the mountains. Because of youthful interest in military affairs the boys began questioning the soldier.

"What war is now going on?" asked the boy in white.

"No war at all," the soldier answered good-humoredly, "but there have been bands of robbers in the moun-

3

tains taking toll from caravans; and Rome not only rules but protects all her Empire. What is your name?"

"My name is Saul," the boy in white replied.

"Then you are a Jew, and surely this other boy looks like a Jew," said the soldier, laughing. "But he is dressed differently."

"That is because I am a Pharisee," said Saul, and proudly pointed to the blue margin on his sleeve and garment. "He is only a Sadducee."

"What is the difference?" The guard showed he did not care what the difference might be. "You are both Jews."

"There is a great difference," replied Saul with importance. "I believe a whole lot more things than he does."

The soldier doubled over with laughter, "It is enough to be a Jew without having to believe more than any other who is a Jew."

Saul turned from the subject and picked up a heavy shield.

"How do you use it?" he asked.

Putting the shield on his arm and using his short sword, the soldier went through his sword exercises. Then, with youthful inquisitiveness, Saul asked what the breastplate was for, and the soldier showed by striking it with his sword that it would withstand heavy blows. Other soldiers came up and Saul, looking up at the sun and noting the time of day, told his comrade that he must go, but the Egyptian grain ship being unloaded attracted the boys.

"The whole world comes to Tarsus," said Saul, as the boys watched slaves carrying great jars of grain out of the ship to the wharf.

"Yes, and the men of Tarsus go out to the whole world," answered the Sadducee boy. "And some day when we grow up, we can go out in the ships."

"You ought to go to Nestor's school, and you would meet boys from all over the world," said Saul, very sagely, "and then you would know something about the world before you got into it."

"In ships," said an Arab who had been standing near, "you will never see the fruits and flowers, nor hear the sweet songs of the birds along the Euphrates where my children are so happy that they do not want to come here with me."

The boys were listening eagerly, but Saul again turned to look at the sun. "I fear I am late now," he said. "I must hasten to my father's shop to my work and my lessons from my grandfather."

He left the wharf and ran down the long street, lined with booths on either side opening into the storerooms—past the dealers in food stuffs, the workers in wood—and wound his way in and out among camels and donkeys until he came to his father's booth, in the upper part of the city. A dark Arab was dealing for a tent and after the manner of his people was telling Saul's father of his country far in the East.

"We do not have the narrow streets of a city like this, through which a man must fight his way among thieves who would rob and merchants who would cheat him. We follow our flocks and herds in the early spring up the clear, cold streams, as the melting snow retreats up the mountain sides, and they fatten without any other worry on our part except to keep away the wolves and beasts that hunger after them. Your tents are our

homes, and they have lasted through many storms.   It is
a shame that we have to pay so much for them."

Saul was listening intently and his father turned to
him, saying:

"Do you think your task will be done if longer you
listen in idleness?"

Saul, shamefaced, hastened through the booth front-
ing on the street into the workroom.   His grandfather
was seated on a raised part of the floor, sewing away at
heavy tent cloth.   In the room was a rude loom partly
sunk in the floor, so that when the weaver went down
into the pit to work he was seated almost level with the
floor.   Saul hurried to his place at the loom, and with
his nimble fingers began the weaving of a coarse dark
cloth made of goat's hair and camel hair mixed.   The
grandfather stopped his sewing and came to Saul to
examine his work.

"This cloth must be woven so tight that it will turn
the water until holes wear in the cloth," he said, "and
each strand must be beaten down in place and not left
loose, as that is."

"If I am to be a tent-maker, why must I take time
to weave?" asked Saul.

"Because you must be able to make the cloth, if need
be, and most of all you must know how to judge the cloth
that you would buy," replied the grandfather, as he
went back to his station.   He added, "Now weave with
every strand a memory of the law.   What is the law for
false teachers?"

"They must be stoned to death," answered Saul
briskly, as he worked the thread of the woof through the
taut warp.

"Nay, that is not such an answer as one of your family must give. You must give the words as I gave them to you. Now answer."

Saul began again, repeating in a monotone:

"If your brother, your son, your daughter,
  Or the wife of your bosom, or your friend
  Shall entice you secretly,
  Saying, Let us serve other gods,
  You shall not consent unto him,
  Nor listen to him;
  Neither shall your eye pity him,
  Neither shall you spare,
  Neither shall you conceal him;
  But you shall surely kill him. . . . .
  You shall stone him with stones that he die;
  Because he has tried to draw you
  Away from the Lord your God."

"That is better. You are to become a rabbi, and you must not be careless in answering at any time what is the law." The old man spoke harshly. "Even if your father does send you to Nestor's school to learn many useless things, you must never be lax in the law. Rabbi Ben Arza sups with us tonight, and he will want to know what you are learning in the law."

During the afternoon Saul recited passage after passage of the old Jewish law to his grandfather, who caught up every failure in the smallest detail.

It is difficult to speak of the grandfather by name, because his name was seldom used. His age was revered, and it was with some regret that he submitted to the proper direction and policy of his son, Ben Hanan, now the head of the house. It was through no disrespect that he was referred to as the grandfather and not by his name, Azel Hanan; rather, it was a sign of the veneration in which Azel was held by his son's family.

Even while weaving the heavy tent cloth and reciting the Law of Moses, the alert Saul would steal a glance through the doorway to see the customers coming in, some with their young sons who were seeing for the first time the city life of Tarsus.

Late in the afternoon Ben Hanan carried the goods displayed in the booth into the storeroom back of it, barred the door and passed through the storeroom into the workroom where Azel and Saul were engaged. While undemonstrative, Ben Hanan critically examined Saul's work and analyzed his conduct. He stopped at the loom to inspect his son's weaving. His eyes feasted on the lad continuing industriously at his work. Then Ben Hanan called attention to the fact that it was near time to dine and led the way into the living-rooms adjoining, where they were as affectionately greeted by the mother and children as if they were returning from a long journey. The six-year-old younger son, David, of whom Saul was very fond, rushed into his father's arms and was lifted up and given the usual kiss. The little sister, a babe in arms, was taken from her cradle and kissed and tossed by all in turn, from the grandfather to Saul.

Deborah, Ben Hanan's wife, a sweet, motherly little woman, flung her arms about Saul, saying:

"How is my Greek boy tonight? Does Nestor's school worry you?"

"It is interesting and easy to me," said Saul. "I have a great advantage over the other boys, for they only know what they learn there, while I have the schooling at home and with Ben Arza. Still, interesting things do come up, dear little mother."

"Have you found anything better than we know?" asked Ben Hanan, coldly.

"Not anything to take the place of what I know and believe, but it is interesting to find out what other people believe, also what they think."

The evening meal was already placed on a mat spread on the floor, and was contained in two or three large wooden bowls into which all the members of the family reached for their food; but before sitting down to the meal, a curious ceremony was performed. Each in turn washed his hands in water poured from a small pitcher by some other member of the family. A basin at the side of the room was used for the purpose.

In the midst of the meal Rabbi Ben Arza came in. He too washed his hands over the basin, in water poured for him by Saul, after which he joined in the eating. His meal was soon finished and he began questioning Saul sharply, while the old grandfather anxiously considered the boy's answers.

"So bright a scholar as is this boy," said the rabbi finally to Ben Hanan, "should not, in my judgment, be tainted with heathen learning, and least of all should he be led away by their athletics."

"In that you are mistaken." The father spoke with finality. "Otherwise he would become a rabbi only to his own people; but if he is well taught and if he is faithful as has been his family for many generations, he will be a teacher among the Greeks and other people, to bring them to see our religion."

"But the waste of time on games and feats of skill," the rabbi was shaking his head dolorously, "is not the part of a Hebrew."

"Our laws are for health and strength," said the father with some animation. "If he can improve his body and gain in strength, as a Jew he is entitled to it."

Looking around, the rabbi discovered that the grandfather was sleeping, his head having dropped on his breast. Ben Hanan went to the old man, gently lifted him to his feet and led him to a mat at the side of the room, where he lay down for the night. The rabbi left, and the whole family soon distributed themselves on mats for sleep, wearing their clothing as was customary.

In the morning Saul questioned his father about what the rabbi had said.

"Is it wrong for me to learn about the history of all people and about their gods?" he asked timidly.

"Not if you are strong, but dangerous if you are weak." The father paused and then said impressively, "If I thought that a son of Ben Hanan was so weak that taunts, ridicule, or boasts would make him doubt, I would not carry out your dedication to become a teacher. Unless you can make a record in that school, you shall stop."

"I can keep up with all in the lectures." Saul looked up in fear to his father. "But the director of athletics discourages me because of my size."

"Keep the pride of your race in your heart. You are of the family of Benjamin, not a weakling. Find your own place. Come home early, for I want you to take up tent-making."

"I am through with weaving?" Saul asked with joy.

"Not through. I said you would take up tent-making." The father spoke severely.

Saul hastened to the school. The lecture-room was a spacious hall with graceful, fluted pillars supporting a high ceiling of thin slabs of marble through which the sunlight streamed in soft rays. In places where the light fell to best advantage were many statues, some of them reproductions of famous figures from the Acropolis in Athens, some the original work of sculptors who had gone out from Tarsus. Stone benches were provided for the students, and there was a stand on a slightly raised platform for the lecturer. Fifty boys about the age of Saul were waiting for the session to begin.

Racially, as well as in their dress and manner, they represented many different nations. Each had his tablet of thin board, on the waxed surface of which notes were to be made with a stylus, since all their information came from the teacher and not from reading books.

Saul came up to the group at the height of a discussion as to whose god was greatest.

"Isis and Osiris are the greatest, for they unite all powers of female and male, and are the ancient gods of all the people who ever went out from the Nile country," an Egyptian youth was saying.

"Long before Egypt had any gods," interrupted a young Persian, "Persia had and still has one god who has all power, and his name is Ormazd."

"I doubt if your gods are older," said Gallio, a Roman youth, with a superior air. "At least none is so powerful now as Jove."

"That is the way. Rome always claims everything," exclaimed Lysander, a fine-looking Greek boy, laughing, "but Zeus *is* the most ancient and powerful, or Rome would not have adopted him under the name of Jove."

During this discussion Saul became very nervous and strove to restrain himself, but at last he burst out in a voice that commanded the attention of all:

"There is only one God, and he is Lord of all."

The kindly old Nestor, who taught the youth in this school, had approached during the discussion and was listening unobserved. The others now turned on Saul in wonder and resentment.

"He is only a Jew. His god never ruled over any people," said Gallio, sneeringly.

All the boys began to shout at Saul, but in the excitement Nestor made his presence known, and soon the boys were in their places on the stone benches, while Nestor took his stand at the pedestal to begin his lecture. All except Saul began writing on their tablets, but Saul's brows were still drawn in a heavy frown, and his face did not lighten until Nestor announced his subject.

"I had intended to speak on a different matter this morning," said Nestor, placing a roll of manuscript on the pedestal, "but your controversy suggests a subject of vital importance to all people of every age. If you would profit by the knowledge of the gods, you should learn that the mature and well-drilled mind finds in the different names and attributes of the gods of different peoples the struggle of mankind to express its highest conception of spirituality. It is not alone the form of the god, not alone the statue that is of most importance; but the characteristics which the worshiper ascribes to his god are of vital importance.

"Whenever a nation has become satisfied with the attributes of its idea of a god, as expressed in a mere formula, and seeks no further knowledge of deity, no higher ideal, then a study of that nation shows invariably a decay in all the finer things which make up a high standard of life among people.

"Whether it be Osiris, Ormazd, Jove, Zeus, Isis, Artemis, the attempt in the beginning is to express in the attributes of deity the best thought and the highest attained spirituality of those who devoutly desire the best possible; but this devotion must be directed to continued effort to express an increasing spirituality. While the Hebrews have never presented their deity in outward form, yet they have sought the one great fact that there is a final source of power and life in the attributes of Jehovah, their Supreme Spirit.

"I would have you remember the words of Aratus, keeping in mind that the poet is using his local name of deity:

> " 'Zeus fills all the city streets,
> All the nation's crowded marts; fills the
> watery deeps
> And heavens; every labor needs the help
> of Zeus,
> His offspring are we.' "

The boys were rapidly writing while Nestor slowly recited the verse, except Saul, whose lips were moving as if repeating carefully several times what Nestor spoke. At the close the Roman pointed at Saul and said:

"All have recorded the words of the teacher save the Jew."

"Your tablets will melt," exclaimed Saul hotly, "but I have a Hebrew's trained memory."

"Let us avoid bickerings," said Nestor quietly. "I have often praised the training of memory among the Hebrews. Saul, can you repeat the verse?"

Saul stood forth and repeated the whole of the verse. Nestor followed him closely with smiling approval, and the other boys carefully read their tablets. When Saul had finished without a mistake, Nestor dismissed them for the gymnasium.

The boys swept into the gymnasium in great tumult of shouting and shoving, and hastened to the dressing-room. Shortly they reappeared, stripped for the races. The director arranged the boys according to size, in groups of four, and started them in trial runs around the arena. Saul was in a group of small boys and came out easily ahead. The director then took the winners of each group and arranged them in new grouping. Again Saul was victor in his group.

"This will be all the running for today," said the director. "Tomorrow I will select those to try for the finals. Put on the cestus and we will have a boxing lesson."

The boys ran to the supplies close at hand, and began winding for each other the strips of cloth about the wrist with many thicknesses over the hand, constituting the cestus for training—the equivalent of the modern boxing glove. Gallio went by himself and wound his own cestus. At call of the director they appeared in the arena, arranging themselves in pairs.

"Can you box as well as memorize, you Jew?" said Gallio to Saul.

"I will play the game with anyone in the game," replied Saul quickly, and ranged himself opposite the Roman youth.

"This is not a fair match in size," said the director

"I am willing to take my chance," Saul retorted, "because he challenged me."

The director laughed and said no more, but gave them a few lessons in leading and feinting, by example. He then stepped back and gave the signal for the many pairs of boys to begin boxing.

All were in good humor and enjoying the sport. Gallio had a smile on his face. On account of his size, he had a longer reach which made it necessary for Saul to crowd close in, in order to land a blow. The director was watching this contest very closely. Saul received a blow on the jaw that staggered him. He recovered and came in closer to his adversary, receiving a blow on the temple that knocked him down. He started to rise, and the Roman jumped quickly to strike again, but the director's practiced eye had seen what happened, and, leaping in, he caught Gallio's right hand and held it while Saul rose. There was a bleeding cut over his eye.

"Nay, I will hold this hand," insisted the director, holding Gallio in a viselike grip. As Saul rose, the director examined his wound.

"We will unwind this cestus," said he, suiting the action to the word. Beneath a few folds of the cestus on Gallio's hand, he found a slug of copper.

"You are barred from the game, because you do not play it according to the rules," cried the director savagely to the Roman youth.

"Not so," said Saul. "Strip off the slugs and make him box. I promise not to beat the air. I would win or lose honorably."

The director smiled at Saul's courage, and, following his suggestion, took another slug from the other cestus of the Roman. The boys gathered around to enjoy the contest. Having learned the danger of staying away from his opponent, Saul began the battle with fierce determination and close-in boxing. In wild excitement the boys cheered them on. In the rapid exchange of blows, Gallio tried to get away from Saul, but the latter followed him too closely, and finally the Roman received a blow which sent him down. Saul stood waiting till he rose. In a flash the Hebrew was again upon him, raining his blows so fast that Gallio could do nothing more than try to protect himself; and he went down again. He lay still for a short time, and then, partly raising himself, held up his hand in token that he was vanquished. Rising, he extended his hand in friendship, smiling at Saul.

"I have learned one great lesson from you," he said, "to play the game according to the rules. Forgive me. Let us be friends."

"You only allowed an old prejudice of your people to rule you," replied Saul, taking the proffered hand, while the blood trickled down his face. Then, smiling, he repeated the words of Nestor:

"We must remember the words of the poet: 'His offspring are we.'"

"Your spirit is greater than your body," exclaimed the director in admiration, placing his hand on Saul's shoulder. "You are not large enough to qualify for the boxing contests, but you may be able to enter the foot races."

"It is fine to strive to win," said the director. "But it is great to be honorable in any sport. Tomorrow we will take our lesson in swimming."

CHAPTER II

MARK ANTONY'S GIFT

Early in the afternoon, Saul was seated by the side of his grandfather, learning how to make the broad, double seam. No word had been said by the grandfather, and Saul was deep in thought over the morning lecture. The controversy among the boys and Nestor's generalizations gave him deep concern as to the application of the Law of Moses.

"Does the law concerning stoning apply to Gentiles?" he asked.

"If it did, we would have to give our full time to them," replied the old man. "Our laws are for Hebrews who cannot be led away by those of another belief."

"Cannot other people find out God?" was Saul's next question, which caused the grandfather to stop in amazement. Long he gazed upon the lad.

"They might know him—all people are bound to know something of God," he finally replied, and then with an impressive shake of his forefinger at Saul, he added, "But they cannot know how to serve him, to gain his favor, except they come within the law."

After a few moments of serious thinking, with idle fingers, Saul asked:

"How did Abraham come to learn of God?"

"That was different." The grandfather's fingers became idle in turn while he pondered his answer, pleased with the boy's searching questions. "Abraham was an exceptional man who by his faith won favor, and it was

17

revealed unto him.   Then our father Abraham handed
down the revelation to us.   We have no more men of
such sublime faith."

"But could there not be a man with as much faith as
he had?" Saul persisted.

"There might be; yes, there will be one day."   The
eyes of the old man brightened and became set as if he
had seen a vision.   "So it is written; but it will be for
some other purpose, for we now know God.   Hasten
with your work now, else you will make no showing for
the day."

Both worked busily for a long time in silence, but
between his stitches the old man would steal a searching
glance at Saul.   Then Ben Hanan, Saul's father, came
into the shop, and in scrutinizing the work done by Saul
he noticed the bruise and the dried blood on Saul's forehead and temple.

"Why this?" Ben Hanan touched Saul's forehead
and spoke severely.

"It was at the games."   Saul was very busy with his
work.

"Tell me, for I must know."   The father's hand upon
Saul's head turned the lad's face up to him.

Saul began to tell him about the boxing, and became so excited that he rose to his feet and went
through the motions, showing how he was struck and
fell; how the director had grasped the hand of the
Roman and unwound the cestus, disclosing the hidden
metal.

"Brutal, brutal!" exclaimed the grandfather.   "It
comes from permitting him to go among those Gentiles.
I oppose it."

"Never mind that just now." Ben Hanan spoke kindly to his father and turned again to Saul. "Tell me all. Surely that is not the end of the matter."

"It was not." Saul forgot all fear of his father as he proceeded with the story of the contest.

Ben Hanan, with all his austerity and dignity, forgot tradition, forgot his exalted idea of his son set apart as a teacher, and with flashing eye and sympathetic nod of the head followed Saul's recital to where Gallio had extended his hand.

"He seemed generous and honest in his offer to be friends." Saul hesitated in embarrassment as his father stared intently at him, but went on as if forced to do so, "so I took his hand and we forgave each other."

"It is well, but we are Romans and not subjects of contempt for these patricians or their sons," said Ben Hanan, drawing himself up proudly.

"I know you have said that before, but I do not see how that can be," said Saul.

"Listen now to my father, and let it sink deep into your mind," answered Ben Hanan. Then he turned to the old man, "Tell him the story."

The grandfather laid his work aside and with a fervor evidenced by his rapid and increasing gestures, plunged into his story.

"Mark Antony, the triumvir, years ago established himself in Tarsus. As ruler of this section of the Roman Empire, he drew around him the great generals of the Far East. He did not drain the wealth of the provinces by taxation, but was generous with the funds that came to his hands. Finally, he sent word to Cleopatra, the merciless and resourceful queen of Egypt, ordering her to come to Tarsus and surrender her kingdom into his hands. Months went by, and he frequently heard of the great preparations that she was making to present herself in such state that she would appear as an equal and not as a vassal paying homage to her ruler. He thought to dazzle her with the glory of Rome's eastern government and he aroused the interest of the whole city. Officers strained every effort to raise the funds needed; and some urged that a special tax be laid, some that the wealth of the Hebrews be confiscated—a plan which Antony refused, with his usual high-mindedness.

"Many notables were gathering for the event, and it became a question of the city preserving the ancient fame of Tarsus."

The pride of the old man in his narrative had brought a glow to his cheeks and his thin form straightened with a momentary return of a vitality long passed. He continued:

"I felt that the time had come for us to show our loyalty to Tarsus, and our appreciation of Antony's impartial and liberal treatment. So, going among the Hebrew merchants, we raised a large sum for the completion of beautiful structures already under way along the water-front and leading to the governor's palace.

"I want you to remember," the old man stood in pride as he finished his story, "the candid courtesy with which Mark Antony, whatever his weaknesses, received us and our donation. In token of his appreciation he sent to each of us who went before him a rescript, investing each of us, our children, and their descendants without limitation, with the full rights and privileges of Roman citizenship, establishing us forever as citizens of the Roman Empire."

Lifting a heavy board in the dais on which he had been sitting, the old man took out a parchment carefully rolled in a piece of leather.

"Always remember," the grandfather said impressively to Saul, unrolling the manuscript, "that you are a Roman citizen by birth, and that is the reason you have the Roman name Paulus. This was a gift, for he did not send it until after Cleopatra had appeared in all her barbaric pomp and had shown herself impressed by the magnitude of the power of Rome. I shall never forget the gorgeous scene when her craft was rowed to the pier and she was led into the shade of the flower-crowned columns and along the glistening way to the steps of the palace. True, it was an evil day for Antony, yet the queen's complete and gracious surrender to him was enough to turn the head of any man. Yea, even Solomon lost his judgment in the presence of such splendor."

As if ashamed of his pride, the old man took the parchment again from the hands of Saul and replaced it within the dais, immediately seating himself and beginning his work. The father returned to the front of the shop, and Saul too resumed his work, though in a dreamlike state, which lasted until the time of the evening meal. When Ben Hanan appeared again, with his usual austere manner, he carefully examined Saul's work and found a place that had not been stitched carefully.

"This must be finished before you eat," said he, pushing his fingers through a place in the seam. "Would that be work of which our family is proud?"

Saul seized the piece quickly and sat down to his task, and Ben Hanan followed the grandfather into the living-room. After the ceremonial washing, the mother asked after Saul, and almost tearfully pleaded with the father:

"He is so young, so new at the work, that it seems hard to demand of him finished and perfect work, and I know that he is hungry." She turned as if to call Saul in, but Ben Hanan laid his hand on her shoulder.

"Do not let your affection spoil the lesson of duty, Deborah," said he tenderly, and turned her again to the meal. She sat down obediently, but every little while kept stealing a glance to the door of the workroom.

The family were nearly finished eating when the door opened and Saul came in brightly. He spoke to his father while pouring the water on his hands.

"I finished that seam, and I am glad I did it now instead of waiting. I learned that I must watch my work and not take it for granted that I have done it right."

Ben Hanan exchanged a meaning glance with the mother. She looked admiringly at Saul and noticed the cut on his forehead.

"What has happened?" she almost screamed in her fright.

"Not much of anything," answered Saul, glancing at his father appealingly. "It does not hurt."

"It is all right, Deborah," the father assured her. "He has told me all about it. Some trifling thing that happened at the gymnasium."

"I am so afraid of the gymnasium," said the mother, "and it may happen again."

"Do not worry," said the father. "It will not happen again."

The meal was finished, and the family were sitting about the room on rugs, when Eleazer, a neighbor, with his wife and his little daughter, Tabitha, ten years of age, came in to spend a social hour. Eleazer and Ben Hanan were soon deep in conversation; the mothers were busy with their needlework and household news. Saul went to Tabitha, who was working on some dainty embroidery, sat down close beside her, and began teasing her in boyish bashfulness by pulling at the thread she was using. She resented it in mock anger and diverted his tormenting by being greatly concerned about the wound on his head.

"How it must hurt!" she said, tenderly touching the wound.

"Mother must not hear," said Saul, leaning his head close to hers, "but in the boxing today a Roman boy struck me with a metal weight concealed in his cestus."

Tabitha's interest in his story was far too great for needlework, and she dropped it in her lap while he told her all about the episode. They sat with mouths and ears close and talked in subdued tones.

"I am so glad that you forced him into a fair contest," she said.

"The director tells me I am not heavy enough for the boxing contest," said Saul regretfully.

"I am glad of it, though I know you would win," said Tabitha.

"Still, I have a chance to get into the foot races," said Saul with a superior air, "but as you are a woman you will not be able to see them."

"Then I will hear all about it," said Tabitha contentedly, "and I may hear of you when you go to school in Jerusalem."

"I want you to hear from me, so that we will know each other when I come back," said Saul.

"While I want to hear from you," said Tabitha, coyly, "you will not care about us in Tarsus, for you will find beautiful maids in Jerusalem."

"There may be beautiful women there," said Saul in very measured tones, leaning his head over closely to Tabitha and looking searchingly into her eyes, "yet I will come back to Tarsus; and I want a girl of this city for my wife."

Tabitha looked at him with wide-eyed gaze, then hurriedly picked up her work and bent her head near to it. At that moment Saul was called by his father.

"Let us speak in Aramaic," said Ben Hanan, "that we may not forget our mother-tongue. Saul, recite the ten words in our own language."

Saul recited for awhile, after which conversation became general. Rabbi Ben Arza came in and, without anyone rising, he took a seat among them.

"If Saul be chosen for the races, I want you all to see the games," said Ben Hanan to the men.

"What foolishness," said the grandfather, wagging his head, "for a Jew to enter an animal-like contest!"

"I do not know of any Jew who ever took the time to strive for the empty honors of these contests," said the rabbi.

"What profit," asked Eleazer, "can there be in mind or purse to a Jew to compete?"

"You are talking of mere custom among Jews," said Ben Hanan, "but if a Jew be in the race you would like to see him win. That is the reason I have arranged for seats for all of us at the games, for I believe Saul will be in the races."

"We may feel that we must go, because of your urgent request," said the rabbi, "but if we can feel no interest in the contest, Ben Hanan, you must not be offended."

"Of course, of course," Ben Hanan gave one of his rare smiles, which was more an expression of shrewd thought than of pleasure, "but if I am not greatly mistaken, there is down deep in every Hebrew a sporting appreciation of the man who strives, and especially if he should win."

The visitors were rising to leave, and Saul went over to Tabitha and mischievously pulled out some of the stitches in the work she held in her hands. She snatched it away from him.

"What is it you work on so carefully?" asked Saul.

"If you win in the race," she said sweetly, "some day I will let you see it."

The men and women lingered long in their parting, but at last the leave-taking was over. The lamps were extinguished after the mattresses were unrolled, and the family lay down to sleep.

CHAPTER III

STAYING TO THE END

The sun was appearing along the high peaks of the Taurus Range of mountains to the north, bringing them out in sharp outline against the purple shadows to the west; the night fog was scurrying out to sea, while Saul hastened to the Greek school. He had in mind the questions he had been asking the grandfather and, while loyal to his training in the Law of Moses, he had a great desire to find out what were the views of the liberal and wise Nestor.

There was often opportunity to ask questions. In that day of intellectual activity, the teacher believed that whatever question he might evoke from his students was an evidence of advancement and a key to the trend of thought to be directed.

The first of the students to hail Saul was Gallio, who came to meet him.

"I tore myself from the caressing arms of Morpheus this morning, O Jew," said Gallio, with half-mocking, half-earnest speech, "to be here early, to know whether your injury was severe."

"It was not bad enough to rob you of your gentle slumber," answered Saul, mocking in his irony, "for we Romans would bear much worse blows and not whine."

"We Romans!" said Gallio in surprise. "Has it made you beside yourself?"

"Nay, be not anxious." Saul still kept a haughty manner. "We are friends. You must remember that

I am a Roman citizen, but to call me a Jew is not offensive."

"Is this a riddle? If so, I do not know the answer." The Roman spoke with more candor.

"It is not a riddle, but a plain fact with which I charge your memory, along with the recollection of our friendship," said Saul with emphasis.

At this moment Nestor came in among the other boys assembled and walked over to Saul and the Roman. He placed his hand on Saul's bare head and glanced at the tiny wound on his face.

"A cut from some dull instrument, but not serious," said Nestor, as if talking to himself, and then, as if for the first time noticing both boys, he added, "I am glad to see you boys in friendly conversation."

"Yes, we are friends, as much as may be," said Saul with sly humor. "In the words of Aratus, 'His offspring are we.'"

"The words may have a thrust I do not understand," said Nestor.

"We know and mean to remember," said Saul, and the Roman nodded assent.

"O Nestor," asked Saul, "how are we to find out the true words or who speaks them about the Supreme Being or Spirit?"

"That is a difficult question," replied Nestor, and the boys gathered around, for they knew that such questions were likely to bring out the most interesting answers. "To refuse the weight of authority to great thinkers of this or any age is to cast adrift on an unknown sea in a starless night; and to follow blindly and implicitly any teacher would be as absurd as to try to become a seaman by living in a boat that is anchored."

"Then what is the solution," asked the Roman, "if the gods are not to be trusted?"

"I said nothing about doubting the gods," answered the old teacher firmly, for he well knew the prejudices with which he had to deal. "But no man can know what the gods approve, except he himself has earnestly tried to know the will of the gods. It finally comes to a question of every individual, for himself, determining and appropriating the knowledge and spirituality that shall control his life."

"What has been revealed is the end of revelation," spoke up a young Greek.

"Not so," answered Nestor quickly, "else there would be an end to the joy of living. Even as we are all looking forward to a time when there will be a return to the Golden Age, or a new and better age, so we must be acutely sensitive to catch any revelation that may direct us to serve the coming-in of the better age. What I would impress at this time is that every man must think rightly for himself, which means that he must first know what the great thinkers have found out, what has been abandoned as useless in that thinking; and thus, holding fast to that which has been found substantial and eternal, he must strive to know more about the divine nature."

"Can we know what is right?" asked Saul.

"Without question," replied Nestor, "for in this exercise of the mind I am advising, a man should commune with his own soul and not yield to his selfish desires."

"How will we know what to accept or reject, save someone tell us?" persisted Saul.

"No one can tell you in each instance what to accept; but it is the training of your youth and the courage of your mind in honest and unselfish investigation that will tell you, or, in short, that will reveal to you the highest and best things if you think on them." Nestor indicated that the questions were at an end by going to his desk, and the boys began taking notes of what he was saying and reading to them.

When school was dismissed, the boys again hurried to the gymnasium. In a garden near the gymnasium many young men were gathered, drinking wine and dancing with gayly decorated girls. The boys stopped near the entrance and looked on for a moment, watched by the athletic director, who stood farther down the street, frowning deeply. Gallio seized Saul's arm and would have dragged him in, but Saul resisted, so the Roman went in alone. In a few moments he returned with a goblet of wine, which he urged Saul to drink, after which they would join the wild dance of boys and maidens who, with clasped hands, were circling around a fountain. Saul refused firmly and the group, except Gallio, made their way to the gymnasium.

The director met them at the entrance and asked immediately, "How many went to the wine-garden?"

"Only a few from Rome and Athens," answered one of the boys. "They said it would make no difference to you if they missed a day."

"None to me, certainly," replied the director, "but a great deal to them. An athlete must keep his body clean and fit to be a god."

The boys stripped for their exercises. Before beginning to wrestle they rubbed themselves with oil until their bodies glistened.   They were in pairs and each was permitted to throw dirt and sand on his opponent, so that his hands would not slip.   While wrestling a boy would seize a handful of dust and spread it on the body of his opponent.   After wrestling they would look as if they had been daubed with mud to change their color.

The wrestling was of two kinds: one, simply to grab and throw the other, the contest being decided by the first one down;   while in the other style of wrestling, practiced chiefly by professionals, the object was to throw and hold the man down while defense could be made by blows.   At this time the boys were engaged in the simple wrestling, and the director went up and down the line showing them how to grip and illustrating the art of catching an opponent unawares.

After a short session at wrestling, the director arranged them for the racing contest.   There were twelve boys, in squads of four, in the elimination contest. Saul was among the first four racers around the stadium. At the last turn to the home stretch he leaped forward with a desperate effort and, straining his energy to the limit, gained the lead and held it to the goal.   There he dropped panting to the ground and watched the other racers come in at the finish, but soon recovered and eagerly stood up.

"Now," said the director, "all who would like to take a swim hasten to the pool."

All except two ran rapidly to the pool, while the director carefully watched their action.   One of the boys who had remained asked him who would be chosen for the finals.

"The boys who will be in the finals are among those who have gone to the pool," answered the director.

Both boys started to run, but the director detained them, saying, "It would not do you any good now, for I wanted to see who had the will to win, and therefore did not make it a condition that you should swim."

The director hastened to the edge of the pool and called to the boys struggling to outswim one another.

"Do not struggle. Take it moderately, with a long, easy stroke."

Saul came alongside and the director spoke personally to him.

"Swim low in the water, a steady, long stroke. Do not try to speed up, then your swimming will be of advantage to you if ever wrecked at sea. Slower; steady; recover easily from the stroke. That is better. This is not a contest, but a lesson for practical use."

The boys swam gracefully past and the director watched them carefully for some time, and then called them out. They passed him on their way out, and to each he spoke some word.

"Do you feel wearied?" he asked Saul, in a way that hinted he would think it only natural.

"Not at all, now," answered Saul. "Are we to run another race?"

The director smiled and told the boys to scrape themselves clean and meet him at the gymnasium.

The boys applied to themselves and to each other the strigil, a common and very necessary instrument, inasmuch as they had no soaps with which to cleanse the body. The strigil was semicircular in shape, almost like a hand sickle or old-fashioned reaping hook, except that it was bent so as to form a channel with two edges, and the outer end was curved backward so as to conform to different parts of the body. The boys busied themselves scraping the oil and dirt from their bodies, and aided each other in scraping their backs. After they were dressed they lined up in front of the director.

"This selection is made not only because of fleetness of foot," he said very seriously, "although that is necessary, but in consideration of the fine spirit and strong determination of the racer to run to his last breath, with his full strength conserved for the final trial. A foot racer is not a mere animal, but a thinker, who must be willing to sacrifice himself in the contest. He must have not only courage, but the will to win. I will now name those who will contest for the highest honors in the principal race."

He named them over, and indicated that they step to the front as he called them. He first named two Greek youths, Lysander and Lysagoras, and a Roman, Grotius. Then he paused as if in doubt, looked at Saul, whose eagerness shone in his eyes, and motioned to him to take his place in front with the other three.

"We have two Greeks, a Roman, and a Jew to compete for the hardest race, 1,500 pedes," said the director, "and all have been selected on merit alone."

"You need have no fear," said Saul. "If I win, not only will a Jew win, but also a Roman of Tarsus."

The director looked on him approvingly, smiled, and the boys were dismissed.

CHAPTER IV

ROMAN ENVY

Saul went home from the gymnasium in great excitement and told his father of his good fortune. Ben Hanan listened very quietly to his son's account and seemed absorbed in deep thought. David danced about in glee and then ran out to the street to tell the other boys of his brother's good luck.

"If you win this race," said Saul's father after David had gone, "and if the rabbi will give you proper words of approval you may go with us to the feast of the Passover. You were dedicated at your birth to become a rabbi, and if you live up to the high resolves we have made for you, there may be a great name for you."

"I know, father," said Saul in quiet, boyish hesitation, "but I sometimes fear you have builded too much on me. People always pity me because I am small for my age."

"Let your mind tower over giants of strength, and you will be strong where they are weak," said Ben Hanan, looking sternly upon Saul. "You must not allow any fault of body or mind, nor any number of voices to turn you from your purpose. Fix your goal; win it! Now go quickly to your work and your lessons with your grandfather."

In the workroom the old grandfather was leaning against the wall sound asleep. Saul started to speak to him, hesitated, and then, smiling on the old gentleman, sat down on a rug and began sewing the pieces of cloth together.

"Do you think to steal upon me unawares?" said the grandfather querulously, arousing from his sleep. "Do you try to make me think you have been working diligently?"

"Not so, for I have been anxious to ask questions," Saul replied. "Nestor said that all people were looking forward to a new time, a Golden Age to come; but I said nothing lest I should make a mistake."

"True enough, these people look forward to a time when morals will be better; and in truth their manners grow corrupt," replied the grandfather, "but they have no such assurance as those of our faith, that the Lord will send us an Anointed One, a Messiah."

"Tell me who is to be the Anointed One," said Saul.

"That I cannot," answered the grandfather, now busy with his work. "But we are promised by the prophets that a great and mighty one will come to us and lead us as victors over our enemies, and again Israel will sit among the nations of the world."

"Why do Jews scatter about the world?" Saul dropped his work. "Why do they work for other nations and not have the rule over even Jerusalem?"

"There, now, you will become a Greek dreamer, unless you sew those things into the mind stitch by stitch." The grandfather pointed to the task and did not resume until Saul was again working. "Our fathers had to pay the penalty of violating the laws of God, and we were driven out many times. Besides, Jews have never learned how to submit in prosperity to one another, and therefore have failed in every attempt to make a strong government for themselves. They must learn from obedience to foreign rulers how to give, demand, and enforce authority. The pride of our people makes them poor in establishing any government among themselves. When the time comes, the Anointed One will lead us back to our country, and Jerusalem will become the seat of wonderful government."

"Then we have a definite promise of a mighty one?" Saul asked.

"Aye, the words of Isaiah are the words of the Lord— that the Prince Immanuel will come." The old man dropped his work and looked away in a trance. "And because we Pharisees know that there is a resurrection, I long that I may be laid in a tomb in Jerusalem to rejoice in my spirit in that great Day."

"O grandfather!" cried Saul. "I have been chosen for the first four in the foot race on the day of the games."

"What nonsense!" The old man complained bitterly. "To your grave there will be a mark on your brow of that brutal fighting. Sad days these! Our young men wear hats like the Greeks, fight like the Romans, and fill their heads full of the useless history of other nations!"

"But you know," Saul spoke with a superior air, "that I am to become a rabbi to win Gentiles to our faith, and I must know what they are taught to believe."

"Very absurd idea," the old man spoke sorrowfully, "that you have to know what other people think about when your whole duty will be to tell them about God. I did not so train your father, Ben Hanan, but he thinks to make you powerful by racing like a Greek. Let us hope that you will not become a professional racer."

At that moment Ben Hanan came into the room and stood listening to the last words of the old man. He smiled pleasantly.

"Let us rather hope," he said, "that the boy will be an honor to us."

The father carefully inspected the work that Saul had done, while David, the younger brother, cuddled down beside Saul and waited in silence until his father had left the shop.

"When are you going to play ball with me?" he asked as soon as the father had gone.

"I am such a busy person that I can hardly say when," said Saul, with the air of a man burdened with many affairs. "In the mornings I must attend the school of Nestor and take my training in the gymnasium. The Roman and Greek boys have the rest of the day to themselves, but I must do this work and get my lessons in the law from our grandfather, and take special lessons from Rabbi Ben Arza. You will find out when you are as old as I am how much harder is the task set for a Jew than for a Gentile."

"Yes, I know," replied David, "for mother told me I must not tease you; but you know so much more about the game than the boys I play with."

"I would play this evening," said Saul, touched by his little brother's gentleness, "but I have to go for a special lesson with Rabbi Ben Arza. Tomorrow we will play, if you will get another boy, so as to make a three-toss game."

"I love my brother," said David, throwing his arms around Saul's neck and kissing his cheek in the simple custom of his people, "and some day, when you come

back a rabbi, I will be doing this work for you."
Immediately he jumped to his feet and ran to the door,
pulling from behind it a boy of his own age who had been
waiting for him. "He will play with us tomorrow
evening," he shouted.

"And we will learn the game so we can beat the other
boys," said the boy who had been in hiding.

"It is a big thing for us," said David as they went
out, "for Saul is in the first four who run in the big
race."

The room became quiet, and Saul began the recitation
of the Law of Moses which his grandfather demanded of
him. With patience and spirit he followed in what to
many would have been a task, but which he mingled with
the ambitions instilled by his father to become a teacher
of his own people as well as the teacher of men who were
not of his faith. He had come to believe that no other
career could compare with this laid out for him to
persuade men by his knowledge that faith in the God
of Jews was more to be desired than the belief or mere
acknowledgment of belief in the gods which he saw
represented in the statues in the public places.

In the cool shade of the court of the dwelling set
apart for the sons of wealth sent from distant places to
gather wisdom from Nestor's school in Tarsus, meanwhile, Gallio was holding forth to the three boys who,
with Saul, had been selected to race for the honors of the
first four.

"I do not care much," said Gallio, "for being shut
out of the races by the director. These teachers are all
right in their ideas of strict rules of conduct for you people

of the East, but in Rome a man of public affairs must know how to mix with the pleasure-seeking men of wealth. I only cared to see the new dance which the girls of the wine-garden were giving."

"He seemed to fear that your dissipation would unfit you as a contender," said Grotius.

"I know their fears, but they do not know how strong we men of Rome are," returned Gallio, as if pitying the director. "Neither women, nor wine, nor both can spoil any except some weakling that has come up from a freedman. My younger brother, Seneca, now in Alexandria, went in for the rules and the philosophies when he was here, and now he is older than his father. He hopes to become a teacher of great men. He worships Jupiter and all the gods, but Mars and the emperor will be enough for me. I want a consulship in some place where life is worth living, away from the making of new rules of morality, and not too much knowledge of old ones."

"Very fine, for you," said the Greek, Lysagoras, "but you may find out you are not strong enough to play that game. You lost your chance in the races because of the dancers."

"That was not a loss, but a gain." Gallio laughed heartily. "You may yet be beaten by the Jew, Saul, and what could be more of a loss?"

"That is to be thought of," said Lysagoras, "for he runs on his will after his legs have grown weak."

"You are even now beaten," said Gallio.

"Not yet," said Lysagoras, "but I am thinking of his staying qualities in the elimination races, and I must confess he has the best chance to win of any of us, even if he is a Jew."

"Now listen to me," returned Gallio. "I am not deceived as to his chances. I think he can win unless you boys use cunning. You are nearly as good as he is.

"This race is three times around the spina of the arena, a little arena compared with our great Maximus in Rome. Now you, Lysander, spurt and take the inside at the start. Saul will come up to you and must try to pass at your right. You swing wide before you get to the north end of the spina, as if to swing around the metae there, but crowd him far out. This will give Lysagoras a chance to come in next the wall and swing wide for his turn after he has passed the metae, and to gain so as to be next the wall on the back course. Let Saul come up with him and start to pass on the outside. Then Lysagoras can spurt and again carry Saul out wide before he reaches the south end of the spina on second round, while Grotius will hug the wall and make a narrow turn, and be in the lead at the north metae. There you can make your turn to suit yourself, Grotius, and spurt for the white line at the end of the course."

"Would that be according to the rules?" inquired Lysander anxiously. Gallio gave him a quick look, as if to see whether he were recalling the boxing incident.

"So long as there is no rule against it, and there is none," Gallio said with authority, "there can be no way for the judges to give the race except to the one who first crosses the goal."

"But would it be honorable?" Lysander persisted. "Besides, by your plan no one but Grotius has a chance to win."

"You would better say that you know that without a plan none but Saul will win." Gallio looked earnestly at each boy in turn and asked the question that decided them:

"Would you not rather make some sacrifice than to have a Jew win?"

"Then let us agree," said Grotius, "though I must say that Saul is as honorable as any of the boys I know. I will run the race as you say, even if it is not exactly the way I would wish to win."

"Neither would I suggest this plan," said Gallio with seeming frankness, "were it not that he must be humbled. He likes to boast that he is a Roman, and here is a chance to make him feel that there is something more than title in citizenship. When I get my *toga virilis* upon my return to Rome, I will give my attention to making the rights of citizenship more restricted. Remember your pledges for the day of the festival."

CHAPTER V

THE WILL TO WIN

Saul's life was a very busy one. True to the teachings of his people, he had learned a trade, the trade of his father, a tent-maker; true to the boasts of the Pharisees, he had been instructed in the written law, as well as the traditions of his people, and knew the hope of resurrection. At that period of history, Gamaliel had achieved a reputation of being one of the great teachers in Jerusalem, following in the footsteps of another great teacher, Hillel.

The historian Josephus states that there were "not fewer than three million" Jews gathered in Jerusalem during the feast of the Passover. They came from all parts of the world, the young men to see the Temple for the first time; the old men to see it for the last time, welcoming the possibility that they might pass away while in the city and be buried in some one of its historical tombs.

For months before the pilgrimage the Jews arranged their affairs for this great event. The means of travel were varied. The swarthy dwellers of inland cities came in caravans, so that the roadways were lined with camels, donkeys, and foot travelers. The nations from which these devotees came arranged to meet the unusual demand for accommodations, including ships, and the general conduct of business had to be adjusted to await the return of pilgrims.

Ben Hanan, because of his standing as a merchant, had been able to make ample provision along the route for this most important journey. He would take with him his aged father, now growing feeble, but joyfully looking forward to seeing once more the beloved Jerusalem. Any friend who might suggest to the old man that he would scarcely be able to withstand the hardships of so long a journey received the confident reply that of a surety he would hold out to reach the city; and the return did not matter.

One object of Ben Hanan's ambition was to place his son Saul under the guidance of the wonderful teacher, Gamaliel, in order that a rabbi, trained and equipped, might take his place as a man of learning in competition with the teachers connected with the famous university in Tarsus. It was his purpose to make of his son a skilful teacher, who should defend and even proselyte for the faith of Jehovah; and to that end he must be thoroughly versed in all the reasoning and rhetoric of the finished scholars of Greece and Rome, in the Stoic and Epicurean philosophies, as well as in the subtle learning of his own people.

With a look far into the future, Ben Hanan, from the little ceremony of dedicating Saul at his birth, had planned that this son should be schooled in all the learning of other nations, and at the same time he should be imbued with the relentless zeal of the prophets for the Law of Moses. He had planned, too, that this favored son should not be spared the lessons of industry, and should be animated by the fixed purpose of his race to continue its course to bring the world into harmony with the revelations of the ages of prophecy. In short, his son must be not only a contender for his faith, but he must be possessed of all the polish of Grecian diplomacy, together with full knowledge of the things that made a Roman citizen of value to his nation.

Among the things which Ben Hanan desired for his son was the possession of a strong body. Though not of great stature, he must have well-trained muscles and be schooled in that co-ordination of mind and body accomplished by the specialists in Greek athletics. It was no foolish pride in him that would be satisfied by the victory of his son in the games, but he wanted the boy to have the confidence that would come from contest with others. He wished to take to Gamaliel a student capable, if the day should come, of becoming the diplomatic leader of people far from the immediate influences of the Temple. Therefore, he greatly desired that Saul should be a winner in the games, in order that he might have knowledge of the people and the confident feeling of one who strives to win on his own merits.

The day of the races came at the close of the course in the lectures. The young men would then return to their homes, some to the Far East, to feed the growing desire of knowledge among their people, just arousing "from the torpor of oriental life." The Romans would return to their homes, to lay aside the cloak of youth and take on the cloak of manhood, to become soldiers in the service of their country, administrators of affairs, and, above all, to assert the supremacy and dignity of Rome as the ruler of the world. The boys from Greece would go to a more contemplative life. Their national existence offered little of attraction; it was swallowed up in the Roman Empire. They had the glory of the geniuses of centuries before, a subdued but never wholly suppressed pride in the intellectual life their great men had given to the world; hence, they turned to the study of letters, art, and philosophies. Those from Egypt had little to boast of in their homes, except very ancient glories, now submerged in the Greek culture, except for the strong and growing influence of the Jewish element, which had taken over the control of some small cities and some parts of great Alexandria.

Not only would the winner of any contest in the games have some knowledge of the people of different parts of the world, by association with representatives of different countries in the school, but his name would go out to the many cities from which these students came. Ben Hanan carefully calculated the values of such training for his son, for he was going counter to Jewish customs and even against the counsel of his own household. It was not that he merely hoped his son might be a winner in the games; but it was his hope that the boy would become a man who would be a leader of men of many nations gathered in Tarsus. Hard though he seemed to be with his son, yet deep in his heart was the hungry ambition for that son's success, in which he would glory.

The chaplet of leaves, in imitation of the crown of sacred laurel given at the Olympian games, was of no value and soon faded, but it denoted the victor. That was the real prize—victory. Old and young came to these games to enjoy the thrill of the contests, and thus to keep alive in the far-off provinces the spirit of Rome, now in her glory, though soon to wane.

The important day of the games came, and the men of Tarsus gathered in the arena. It was unusual for many Jews to be present. The seats were filled when the master of ceremonies led the parade around the arena. The proconsul, with a guard of mounted lictors, was at the head of the procession in a richly decorated chariot drawn by four beautiful stallions, prancing as if proud of their place of honor. Two sets of brightly burnished fasces, symbols of Roman power and authority, were placed in the chariot so that the proconsul stood between them. Two elephants suggested the greater display of Rome. Then followed two- and four-horse chariots, which would compete in the arena, and horsemen riding bareback, who would exhibit feats of riding.

The boxers, wrestlers, and foot racers followed afoot, stripped as for the contests, to give the people a chance to make their choice of winners, for the populace had as much enjoyment in making wagers on the results as in the exhibition itself.

While the parade was in progress, Ben Hanan arrived with his father and Rabbi Ben Arza. A large number of Jews had been at the entrance since the gates opened, waiting until Ben Hanan would come, as he had told them he would, to enter with him. They had reserved a section opposite the south end of the spina, and had a close view of the white mark that was the goal of the races. They attracted much attention as they filed in and filled the seats. Farther to the north and on the same side of the arena were many of the young men from the school, who were getting out of the day that vast enjoyment which youth has always been able to extract from any parade, great or small.

"The Jews have come to see their champion lose," said Gallio, laughing and pointing to the company of Jews, as they selected their seats with some hesitation.

Ben Hanan had a seat in the front row, with his father and Ben Arza back of him. Immediately the rabbi and the grandfather began a conversation in which they interested most of their friends, turning away their faces as if the arena had no interest for them.

After the parade there was a two-horse chariot race which aroused the interest of the people, but none of the Jews save Ben Hanan and one or two others observed it. Then followed a four-horse chariot race, which so aroused the people that the confusion of cries disturbed the very earnest conversation of the rabbi and the grandfather.

A number of young men gave an exhibition of boxing which enabled the two conversationalists to get deep into some controversy as to the interpretation of the law; and to show how little they cared for the sports they turned their backs toward the arena.

The master of ceremonies was announcing that the next on the program would be the first four contestants for the honors of the hardest race to be run, three times around the arena, in which the young men who had qualified were Lysander of Corinth, Lysagoras of Athens, Grotius of Rome, and Saul of Tarsus.

The grandfather turned to the arena, and could not hear any more conversation.

"I maintain the exclusive authority of the Torah," said Ben Arza, plucking at Azel's sleeve to get his attention.

"Saul, my grandson, is in this race," said the old man, "and the Torah is safe. How small he looks when stripped, and I am almost ashamed to look on his naked body!"

"He is sturdy and no doubt strong," commented Ben Arza, giving closer attention.

Ben Hanan was so rigid that he plainly disclosed his great anxiety and the fierce control he maintained over his emotions. He paid no heed to the shouting boys on his left. Gallio rose, and drawing a purse from his girdle, swaggered over to Ben Hanan.

"O Jews," cried Gallio, shaking the bag in front of Ben Hanan, "here is the gold sent me for my expenses on my return home. Should I lose it, I would have to spend many more weeks in Tarsus, because of my folly, waiting for another remittance. Yet I cannot resist the chance to wager it that Saul will not win this race, if so be that any Jew thinks he can win."

Ben Hanan looked at him closely and asked, "Is your name Gallio?"

"You have said it, father in Israel," returned Gallio mockingly, "and would that induce you to have my company in Tarsus?"

"Not so, my son," Ben Hanan was rising while he spoke, "but if the gold remain in your purse, it will not cut so much as if it were copper on your hands."

Gallio was so taken aback by this reply that he could make no retort and went back to his companions much crestfallen. Ben Hanan left the company and hastened down to the doorway opening on the race course. Saul was warming up, as were the others, and Ben Hanan beckoned to him to come nearer.

"Son, be wise and careful." Ben Hanan showed his deep anxiety in the stress of his voice. "I have just listened to Gallio, offering to wager against you. His manner is so certain and so brazen that I am sure there is some trick planned against you, which he knows. Use every art that the rules will permit, and win, that this boastful Roman may be humbled."

The master of ceremonies was calling the contestants to their places. Ben Hanan hastened back to his seat.

"You will not chance any money?" asked the old grandfather.

"Nay, more than money—my hope," returned the father.

"This is so tiresome," said the old man, leaning back in his seat, "that I wish I had left before this race was called."

The boys were ranged in an order determined by the casting of dice. Lysander was on the inside, next the spina, then came Saul, Grotius, and Lysagoras. A broad, white line extended from wall to wall of the arena south of the spina; and on the right side this line was the starting-point, on the left side, the goal.

The arena was oblong. A little to the left of the center of the long way was a low wall, extending throughout the central part, leaving a wide space between each end of the wall and the inclosing walls of the arena. This central low wall was called the spina, and at each end of it were three small pillars, called metae. In chariot races, some of which were seven times around the arena, it was one of the arts to make the turn so as not to lose speed, and yet to come back into the course without too much distance being covered; and often the drivers would swing out before reaching the end of the spina and swing in so close to it that the wheels would be wrecked against the metae. The spina was narrow and some of the charioteer's problems in turning at the metae confronted the foot racers, but in lesser degree.

High walls inclosed the arena. From the top of these walls the seats of the audience rose in tiers to the inclosing outside walls of the whole structure. The decadent days, in which women attended, as was later the custom in Rome, had not come to Tarsus. Here the Greek influence prevailed, and the audience crowded the great seating capacity, to enjoy the races and contests in which the participants esteemed it a privilege and an honor to take part. The Romans held to the view that slaves, captives, and hirelings should appear in the arena for the amusement of the people, while the Greeks excluded slaves and hired performers. Their games were their expression of religious regard for the development of the body; and on this day in Tarsus the old Greek admiration of beauty and passion for the best form of athletics prevailed. The wide spaces for the spectators were crowded with all classes of people, including the most learned and the highest of rank.

The director of the gymnasium, proud of his position, stood in front of the boys, as they lined up in running order, and spoke a few last words:

"Let everyone do his best and remember his training. Remember, this is the hardest race, 1,500 pedes. You must conserve your strength and not waste yourself in vain spurts. To have run in this race and lost after an earnest effort is some honor."

The director stepped back, slowly lifted a white napkin, and paused to give the boys a moment in which to adjust themselves. The grandfather leaned forward and held his breath. Ben Hanan rested his chin on his hands, on the railing in front of him.

The director dropped the napkin, and the boys leaped to the race. Down toward the first turn they sped. Grotius dropped back of Lysander, with Lysagoras running close beside Grotius. If Saul attempted any speed Lysander leaped with him, for Lysander knew that his spurting would not do more than cause him to lose the race, and that was inevitable, according to the compact. He crowded Saul wide to the right, as if to swing in close to the metae on the back turn.

At the turn Lysagoras was in close to the wall and Grotius was following him. Ben Hanan saw that the distance for the swing into which Saul was being forced was too great, for already his lead of Lysagoras and Grotius was nearly taken up. Would not Saul see the trick? Ben Hanan asked himself.

Lysander was pressing Saul out farther from the wall. Saul slowed up for a few paces so that he leaped from behind and ahead of Lysander in making the turn at the north metae. With a short spurt Saul came in behind Lysagoras and ahead of Grotius who was saving himself for the final lap. The cheers and jeers from the vast audience showed that the spectators keenly appreciated the effort to crowd Saul into loss of time and that his finessing for gaining his place in the race aroused wild enthusiasm.

The racers settled down to a steady pace, warily watching one another, and keeping their relative positions—Lysagoras leading and next the spina, closely followed by Saul, then came Grotius and Lysander. In this order they had turned the north metae, and were racing down the last half of the second lap toward the south pillars. The audience had been tense and silent. One more round was to be run, the desperate struggle to hold to the end. Spurting was dangerous to any racer.

Saul speeded up a few paces. Lysagoras leaped to keep even with him, and began crowding him out for a wide swing around the south metae. The audience rose as if impelled by one mind sensing a thrilling move about to be enacted. Saul slowed a few paces and Lysagoras slowed in time with him. The jeers of the audience swelled in a voluminous snarl.

Opposite the south metae Saul slowed his pace as if to drop behind Lysagoras who immediately slowed his pace. Then Saul leaped, spurting in front of Lysagoras, and swung in close to the metae barely missing treading on the heels of Grotius who was making his outward swing on the farther side of the metae. Saul was next the spina, Grotius, coming in from the sweep into which his momentum had carried him, was a little in advance.

The audience had watched in tense silence the rapid maneuver, then joined in the wildest cheering. Above all the roar could be heard the high-pitched voice of the grandfather, screaming:

"Run, thou son of Kish! Run!"

People had risen from their seats and voices were cheering madly for Saul, with a few scattering shouts for Grotius. Ben Hanan sat, tense, concentrated to a painful degree, his chin resting on his hands, his eyes shifting only enough to follow Saul. The grandfather had come down to the balustrade and was gesticulating wildly over the arena. He had torn his turban from his head, loosening the folds, and it was now merely a streamer of cloth, which he swung as he leaned far out over the railing, crying:

"Run, run, thou son of Kish! Run! Fly, fly, thou gazelle, fly!"

The rabbi also was leaning over the railing, shouting for Saul; and the rest of the Jews had crowded down so close, in their excitement, as to endanger those who sat in the front seats, nearest the balustrade.

Along the spina the boys were running, with Grotius on the outside slightly in the lead. This was the coveted position and gave him the choice of making the turn at the pillars wide, either at the approach or on the farther side. He held close to the spina and allowed his momentum to carry him wide beyond the metae.

Just before they reached the north metae Ben Hanan left his seat, and ruthlessly shoving out of his way all who opposed him strode over to Gallio, who was leading the shouts for Grotius. Gallio looked up into the older man's face and saw there such signs of a pent-up deluge of hate, vengeance, and energy ready to burst that he started involuntarily. Ben Hanan's fingers were twitching nervously. Gallio had no fear of men, but that figure towering over him was not man, it was conscience, and he trembled. As he ceased shouting, the others in the company became quiet. That foreboding figure was an incarnation of justice. Ben Hanan laid his hand on the back of the seat and faced the arena. All had passed so quickly that Saul's finessing in completing the turn at the north metae could be seen.

When Saul neared this point he slowed his pace slightly and swung in so close that his shoulders barely missed the pillars. He drew a fresh, deep breath and, hugging the wall closely, gathered himself in a mighty effort to increase his speed to the goal. His quivering muscles responded to the new impulse and he sprang forward in a spurt as vigorous as if it were the first part of a short race.

Lysander and Lysagoras were far in the rear. Grotius had been carried on a wide circle by momentum, and Saul was now in the lead. His exhausted muscles responded as if renewed instantly with some magical fluid of life. Every leap was co-ordinated for the distance, as if in that brief space of time he had calculated the number of steps to be taken, the force of every spring, and the speed required. The multitude exulted as they foresaw his revenge.

Wildly waving his streaming turban the grandfather cried:

"Run, lad, speed thee! Run as Cushi ran! Run, thou son of Kish!"

Rabbi Ben Arza had loosened his outer coat in his excitement and was waving it and shouting:

"Speed thee! Speed thee! Swift as the eagle! Saul, Saul, the mighty!"

The other Jews grew wilder in their acclaims. The local pride of the Tarsians was shown in their shouts of encouragement.

The footfalls of Grotius running close behind Saul sounded like thunderbolts in his ears. Time—time— he had lost all count of time! It seemed to him that long periods passed from one spring until his other foot would touch the earth. He felt as if he were not fully touching the ground, he merely skimmed the dust. He dared scarcely breathe lest he fail to leap as soon as his foot touched ground. His strong will held brain and muscles in function, his spring augmented his momentum toward the goal almost before his weight rested on the supporting foot.

Ever so long ago he had turned for the goal. He felt himself flying along the earth; but far, far in the distance was that longed-for white mark. There flashed through his mind often-repeated words of the director: "Do not lose control of yourself when nearing the goal."

It was like a fresh breath. He gripped himself still closer, and desperately drew a new impulse from that mysterious reservoir, the will to win. That was better. He could no longer hear Grotius. He could think to time his spring to aid his flight. Surely the goal was near! Was that a flash of lightning over which he leaped?

He fell in a total collapse in the dust beyond the goal. His world had gone dark.

The director waited until Grotius, a close second, had crossed the goal, then quickly picked up the crumpled body of Saul and carried him to the dressing-rooms, crooning over him as if he were a baby. Tenderly he bathed Saul with cold water until he opened his eyes.

"Now I know," said Saul, gasping between words, but smiling up at the director, "that was not a stroke of lightning, it was the goal. Has Grotius come in?"

The director laughed and nodded, vigorously rubbing the twitching muscles of Saul's legs, rolling him over and over and back again until nearly normal conditions were restored, all the time saying:

"In spite of all, you won. By Hercules, what a heart you have! You won!"

The audience had seen the trick which had been planned to defeat Saul, and jeered Lysander and Lysagoras as they neared the goal, far in the rear. Men were shouting like maniacs, each trying to outscream his neighbors. The people were as one voice. The Jews were submerged in the vortex of enthusiasm. Words were not used, it was the primitive cry of victory.

In a lull of the noise, Azel, now fired with the zeal of youth, his dignity as a grandfather having slipped away, was shouting to no one and to anyone who would listen:

"He can run! He is a son of Kish!"

The Romans with Gallio joined in the cheers and shouts, their racial prejudices quite forgotten. Ben Hanan still stood at Gallio's side, without joining in any demonstration.

"Well, Saul made a wonderful finish," said Gallio to him.

"And it was well for you," replied Ben Hanan, with a world of meaning in his eyes and voice.

He walked back to his place, evidencing his reaction only by a relaxation of his rigid bearing. Ben Arza congratulated him warmly, and the grandfather continued to repeat:

"He is a son of Kish!"

The judges came across the arena toward Ben Hanan, with the naked, quivering body of Saul between them, supporting him as if it were an honor to touch his flesh. At a signal from Saul they stopped under the place of Ben Hanan and, amid a hush that was the utmost silence of a multitude, the judges solemnly placed the victor's crown of leaves on Saul's bowed head.

The cheers again broke out, rumbling like deep thunder along the great distances of the arena and back again. The judges raised their hands for silence and there was a lull, broken, however, by the high, cracked voice of the grandfather, who shrieked to Saul:

"Thou art a son of Kish!"

When quiet was obtained, the judges presented Saul to his father as the victor. Ben Hanan in superb dignity bowed his acknowledgment to the judges and spoke evenly to Saul:

"My son, you did run well."

Those simple words, so quietly spoken, carried a wealth of comfort to Saul. The kind director took Saul's arm and led him back to the dressing-rooms. The crowd was cheering in cadences now, but Saul did not hear the great chorus. Exhausted by the struggle, his mind, as if released from sympathy with his body, was dwelling on the greater prize now assured to him—his life in Jerusalem.

PART II

In Jerusalem

CHAPTER VI

UP TO JERUSALEM

The household of Ben Hanan was busy arranging for his momentous journey to Jerusalem. Clothes for traveling and for use in the city had to be prepared, and an extensive wardrobe was necessary for Saul, who would probably remain in Jerusalem.

Ben Arza plied Saul with questions in review of his studies, and drew from his recollection of his own school-days many intricate problems. He gave him the latest discussions and interpretations of the scribes. Ben Arza thought of the reflected glory there would be in his sending to Gamaliel a student who would challenge the attention of the great teacher.

Because Eleazar would accompany Ben Hanan, the two families were intimately associated in the bustle of preparation. Grandfather Azel superintended the preparation of the food. He compelled the women to put in plenty of dried fruits, bread, and cheese, and to leave out the delicacies.

On the day of departure the people gathered at the wharf far down the lake, before the break of day, to board the ship, which would leave early so as to catch the morning breeze. The lake, 10 miles long, fed by the Cydnus River, lay alongside the Mediterranean, from which it was separated for several miles by low sandhills, through which it finally broke into the sea. Men from beyond the mountains, some with their families, all in distinct groups, together with friends to see their people depart, crowded the wharf and almost shut the ship from view.

This Egyptian ship was 150 feet long, with one large mast a little forward of the center, to which was attached a single large square sail, while on the smaller mast at the bow was a small sail. Two huge oars protruding through the bulwarks, one on each side of the center of the stern, were the rudders. It was on its return to Egypt from Rome. Like all ships, it was sailed only during the daytime, and seldom out of sight of land, tieing up at night in some little harbor, or at the wharf of some seacoast town. This primitive craft (there were some larger) crossed the wide stretches of sea, going from land to land along the coast, and from island to island; even from Alexandria to Puteoli or to Brundisium, the ports of Rome. The corn of Egypt was necessary for the city of Rome.

Knowing that it was the time when pilgrims set out for the Passover in Jerusalem, the captain had put in at Tarsus to take aboard passengers, as far as Caesarea.

In the dim light just before sunrise the commotion was increasing. Bundles were carried aboard and confusion of packages caused confounding of passengers; frequent and noisy inventories of his baggage by each passenger and oral rechecking with those ashore added to the babel. Forgotten messages were given by friends to be delivered in Jerusalem; repeated farewells; admonitions of the departing to those remaining; prayers aloud by those remaining for the departing pilgrims. Family and friendly groups made up for the pilgrimage remained segregated, or at least spent much effort in trying to remain together and separate from the others. Loud and long lamentations were frequent, after the manner of orientals.

The sun was coming up over the eastern hills, spilling its light like molten silver over the placid lake. To the north the great peaks of the Taurus Mountains stood out as if they were monarchs waiting to receive the homage of the world; the deep purple shadows trailing away to the west from their shoulders were their royal robes.

A gentle breeze rippled the lake. The captain of the ship had flogged his slaves to their places and, whip in hand, stood at the top of the plank, loudly commanding his passengers to come aboard.

"Find out Gamaliel's opinion, if tradition must not be thrice sifted," said Ben Arza to the grandfather, on the wharf.

"If strength be given me after hearing once more the Hallel in the Temple, that will I do," said the grandfather, stooping and kissing David's forehead.

Again and again the captain vainly called for his passengers to get aboard. They knew the customs of the country and, knowing them, continued their farewells. The law of custom was that, however much he urged them, they would still take their time. Deborah, her sweet face tear-stained, clasped her son Saul to her bosom. Though he was small for his age, he was as tall as she. He leaned his head on her shoulder; and he saw, near at hand, little Tabitha, through her tear-stained veil looking her heart to him, and holding out a little roll in her right hand, afraid and yet wanting to reach it to him.

Ben Hanan had spoken the final word to Saul and was leading the grandfather up the gangplank. Saul dropped his arms from around his mother and ran to Tabitha.

"I promised to tell you what I was making, if you won the race." She hung her head while holding out the package to him. "Here it is. Take it with you."

"My prize of victory!" cried Saul, taking the package and starting to seize her.

Like a timid fawn yearning for the stroke of its master, but trembling with fear, she shot a glance at Saul that told him the sweet and long story, if put into words, and leaped behind her mother away from him.

Deborah, looking about, saw him standing **as if** entranced with the vision of Tabitha; and, while she laughed and cried, the gentle mother took his arm and hurried him to the ship.

Slowly the ship was pushed away from the wharf and its prow turned toward the outlet to the sea. The early morning breeze was beginning to swell the big square sail, and the ship began to drift with the mists out to the blue Mediterranean. So slowly did the ship move that for a long while farewells were called back and forth from ship to shore. The captain and his crew had to be harsh with the passengers to keep them from so crowding to the shore side of the little ship as to threaten to capsize it. Saul had climbed to the highest point of the elevated structure on the stern of the ship and was waving the little napkin which Tabitha had given him, a delicate piece of needlework with grape vines, leaves, and clusters of grapes, embroidered on finest linen.

Through days of favorable winds, and calms that held the ship fast, with stops at several places, the ship finally arrived at Caesarea. At every port passengers insisted on being taken aboard, until the margin of safety had been overreached, and no one so much as the captain hailed with joy the passage of the ship into Herod's great artificial harbor at Caesarea.

The Roman governors had made this city the seat of government in a vain effort to build a capital that would withstand the ravages of time and rival Jerusalem.

Ben Hanan led his party into the older section of the city, to the house of his friend, Simeon, to whom had been intrusted all needful arrangements for the journey overland to Jerusalem. It was well that such arrangements had been made in advance, for the multitude gathering wildly demanded every means available for their conveyance.

It would take them nearly three days to make the journey. The noonday sun would get so hot that travel would have to be suspended for long hours, to rest the animals and await the cooler evening breezes. The grandfather was mounted on a horse. The father rode a camel, with much luggage. Saul was given a chance to ride a donkey, already well loaded with bundles. Eleazar rode a horse.

In the early morning Ben Hanan and his companions were on the road, well-defined as far as the eye could reach by pedestrians and animals, forming a continuous procession up the gently sloping hillsides to the higher plateau. The spring rains had brought out the grasses and flowers, so that the hills and plains were clothed in beauty, shortly to become a dull brown under the withering heat of the rainless season.

Near midday they reached a deep and narrow defile along which the road hid itself from view, as if detouring,

to come out on the plains above in a surprise attack.
There was a spring of water which had been walled up
and the dirt and sand had been cleaned out, so as to
furnish clear water for man and beast.

This cleaning of wells and watering-places had been
looked after by priests of the Temple, at least thirty
days before the Passover, on all the ways coming into
the Holy City. It was a part of the duty of those
governing the Temple to attend to the wells and to
repair the rude walled khans in which the pilgrims slept
along the roads.

The pilgrims were not a good-natured lot on the
journey, for they felt that those outside of their own
group were strangers until they were within the walls
of the city, and, therefore, in some way (at least by their
presence) contributed to the inconveniences of travel.
Saul noticed that the roadways were not the substantial
paved ways, built by the Romans out of Tarsus.

All the animals and men, like animals, were striving to
slake their thirst from the rock-rimmed drinking-places
and curbed springs. A pilgrim with a camel was drawing
a bucket of water, while another was upbraiding him for
stirring the water. They simply abused each other in
words, without any fear or thought of blows. While
the owner of the camel, holding his filled bucket, paused
to pour forth his wrath upon the owner of a donkey,
the donkey drank the vessel dry. This brought on a
great state of anger, for the camel-driver held to the
primitive idea that the owner of the donkey was responsible for the wrong done by the beast.

The midday meal had been eaten and the grandfather was sleeping in the shade of a tree. Saul was

industriously keeping the flies away from the grandfather with a bough. Ben Hanan was looking out over the resting pilgrims who made up an irresistible tide, flowing up over the hills and down into the city of his fathers. While the characteristics of the race showed on all the faces, the common expression was that of consuming zeal, a zeal not for the nation, but a zeal for a religious idea which found its expression in the Temple and the customs of worship.

Ben Hanan studied the motley throng, composed of tradesmen and artisans from along the coasts of the Mediterranean, sunburned Semites from the deserts of the northern country, and well-groomed merchants and teachers from Egypt. Then his gaze rested on Saul so earnestly that the boy went over to hear what he had to say. Saul sat down by his father, who still seemed to be thinking on his son.

"What a strange thing it is, my son," said Ben Hanan, laying one hand on Saul's shoulder and gesturing with the other, "that God led his people out of bondage, and now holds them in the hollow of his hand. Surely there is some mighty purpose in this, in which Jerusalem and this Holy Land are only a part, even a small part. Where we now rest the armies of the East have met and battled with the armies of Egypt, crushing the Hebrews in the grinding. Century upon century war has swept back and forth across these hills, the northern and southern countries contending, and again the East and the West: Greece conquering Egypt; Rome conquering the world. Why should these people, even as you and I, love these rocky hills? What is the mighty purpose of God? Why this persisting pilgrimage to our altars?"

"I cannot answer now," said Saul, looking up into his father's face as if he had caught the acknowledgment of the longed-for comradeship. "If ever I think I have found the reason or how to discover the reason, I will bring it to you for your thought."

"It is strange how such thoughts come to me whenever I am among these quiet hills." Ben Hanan lifted his eyes off to the distant coast line, across the shimmering heat waves. "There is something in the clear air, the plain hills, the distant mountains, the great stillness —something here seems to give my soul wings; my thoughts fly as easily as those high, white clouds against the bright blue. Then look you, Saul, on these people! Some so coarse as to offend by their mere presence; some so crafty that you fear to meet them; others show that they have been so oppressed that they cringe when they should be cheerful; others are ruthless: yet all deny themselves to make this pilgrimage. Son, learn you the mystery!"

Ben Hanan gazed tenderly on Azel, sleeping heavily, and spoke to Saul:

"I fear he will have his wish to sleep the long sleep in Jerusalem."

Saul took his place again by the grandfather. After a while the old man aroused and in a sprightly way announced that he was refreshed. The bundles were packed on the animals; and, mounting, Ben Hanan's party joined the long line winding up the dusty trail, up, up; and then they came to hilltops from which could be seen in the Far East the mountains beyond the Jordan, blending in with the sky, while between rolled the sea of air that flowed in ripples, as if it were a gossamer veil, hiding the face of the valley from view. Other hills near at hand hid the nearer side of the valley.

At night the travelers stopped at a caravansary provided for pilgrims, in which it was their good fortune to find a place to unroll their matting and rest for the night. And all night long they could hear the padding of the passing camels and the tinkle of their bells, as well as the hoof beat of donkeys and horses, urged on by pilgrims, in their anxiety rushing forward during the cool hours and hoping to secure better appointments in the city by reason of arriving ahead of others.

Ben Hanan's party resumed their journey in the early morning, before the crowing cocks or singing birds had hailed the coming day. Near the noon hour they rested by the side of a well of sweet water, and partook of their refreshments while their beasts of burden ate and rested. The last ridge was in front of them, and then they would drop down upon the valley north of the Holy City. Ben Hanan and Azel slept, but Saul's vivid imagination kept him awake.

After a long climb up the side of the hill they saw at the right the shoulder of a still higher hill, around the base of which their way led. Just when reaching the top the people were stopping and sinking down in adoration.

"What means that worship?" Saul asked his father.

"We, too, may join in it, if so be our minds and hearts understand and feel aright," said the father, in the mysterious manner of eastern speech.

All were urging their animals to a faster pace. Grandfather Azel was pushing past others, so that it was difficult to keep up with him. The last part of the road led straight up the steep hill, for eager travelers had worn a way by the shortest cut instead of following the longer bend of the road.

Reaching the top, there burst on their view the city of their hearts. The sun had passed the meridian, and, through a cloudless sky, revealed the glistening marble of Herod's palace on the western hill, the high-arched bridge spanning the Tyropoeon Valley and connecting the western hill with the Temple hill. The Temple reflected the bright sunlight with added brilliance. In the clear air of that land even the courts and towers through the distance gave a picture in perfect detail. The tower of Antonia stood out as if it were a sentinel on guard. The great walls of the city seemed about to burst from the houses crowding against them. The flat-roofed houses clambered against one another on the hillsides, reaching up for air and light from the crowded space. Tents here and there on housetops looked as if a new city were camping on top of the more solid structure. Tents and arbors had been placed on top of the dwellings to accommodate the throngs at this feast.

Saul had stopped in wonder. Others, in veneration, had dismounted, and pedestrians were already on their knees. Saul saw his grandfather and the others dismounting and he quickly joined them. All kneeled and bowed their heads to the ground; then, lifting up his face, Grandfather Azel began intoning, while the rest of the company repeated with him:

> "Jerusalem is builded as a city
> That is compact together;
> Pray for the peace of Jerusalem;
> They shall prosper that love thee."

Remounting, the party joined the long line stretching away even to the gates of the city. Weary beasts were prodded to a faster and still faster pace. The faithful foot travelers gathered their skirts higher under their girdles and quickened their steps. Pious exclamations were heard on every hand; the tone of anger and petulance was smoothed by a common feeling of joy; eyes that glowered and eyes that stole glances of distrust along the journey now shone with light and enthusiasm. The dust of passing beasts was no longer a cause of vituperation, as it had been on the other side of the hills.

Ben Hanan's manner had been growing warmer toward Saul on the journey, until a comradeship had been established. Now, waving his hand toward the city, he said to his son:

"Rome is called the Eternal City, Athens the Beautiful, but Jerusalem is lovely, the center of the worship of the one true God."

Coming nearer the city, there were places in the faces of the small cliffs freshly whitewashed, and once in a while there would be a whitewashed mound near the roadway.

"I thought those were sepulchers," said Saul to his father. "Why are they whitewashed?"

"You know, my son," Ben Hanan replied, "that no one can go into the Temple service who has not been clean for at least a week, and that the touching of a dead body or burial place makes one unclean. The Levites come out thirty days before the Passover and whiten all the sepulchers, so that any pilgrim, even in the night time, will be warned and will not have to touch a grave."

The widespread cavalcade choked into the Damascus gate and filled up the narrow streets. All was turmoil. Here and there were Levites from the Temple, answering questions, directing inquiring pilgrims to their friends, and disposing of others by allotment to certain houses. Every householder was required to give all possible room to pilgrims, even to placing booths on his roof, and he would sleep in the streets to make room for anyone coming up to worship. Here and there among the crowds a Roman soldier passed, good-naturedly doing police duty in a manner of superior tolerance toward these people in their fanaticism.

The slow, forward movement of the crowd was stopped by an altercation. A heavily loaded donkey, carrying provender for animals, was being prodded along by his driver, and in the jam was nibbling from a pack carried by a man. The man turned to berate the driver. They became so vehement in speaking of each other, and the low character of each other's ancestors back to the third and fourth generation, that they did not notice that a camel was eating from the pack on the donkey. An aristocratic rider on the camel replied to the verbal abuse of the donkey driver, who gave his attention to the camel rider. In the interchange of choicest epithets the aristocrat made no distinction between the donkey driver and his eloquent antagonist, so both of them tried to express their low opinion of the man out of reach on the camel. Words had failed them, and they began spitting at the man on the camel, the most expressive form of contempt known to their people. Saul, from his experience in Tarsus, expected an encounter, but when the men began spitting, he laughed loudly.

"Stop that," a Roman guard cried, roughly turning around the two men on foot. "Fight if you will, but your spitting musses up the street to no purpose."

While Ben Hanan slowly led the way through the dense crowd Saul was alert to get a revealing glimpse, at any street crossing, of the upper part of the Temple, now high above them. After winding in and out among the mass of people, they came into a narrow side street in front of a plain and forbidding double door, high enough to permit a camel to pass through. In front and on each side of the doorway were tradesmen's booths setting back under the first floor, but they were not occupied, for the morning hours allotted to trade had passed. Repeated knockings brought a man to the other side of the small door set inside of one of the larger doors; and, after the names of all in the party had been given and word taken back, the man on the inside returned and opened the door with much show of haste and eagerness to welcome them. Ben Hanan and all of his party dismounted, following the man who led the animals through the doorway to an open, inner court. On one side of the court were stalls for the animals, on another side the storage- and workrooms, and on another side the living-rooms.

This was the home of Ben Gerber, who had married Saul's sister Martha. He was also a tent-maker and dealer. Through the doors of the living-apartments Martha and Ben Gerber rushed to welcome their kinsmen and the friend, Eleazar. In the privacy of this court the women were unveiled, because it was the citadel of the family, sacred from the intrusion of strangers. The warmth of the greetings was typical of these people, who expressed all the emotions of life without restraint.

By the flickering oil lamps the conversation flowed along over the news of Tarsus and Jerusalem until a late hour. Martha mothered Saul until he remonstrated and, to emphasize his near approach to manhood, told of his winning the race.

"But, Saul," said Martha, "you are still so small. You take after our mother's people."

"It is not bulk that counts so much as it is what I have the will to do," said Saul, while his sister smiled appreciation.

"Aye, I have made all the arrangements," Ben Gerber was saying to Ben Hanan. "The day after the morrow we will go to the Temple for our paschal lamb, and I have already bought from a shepherd a fine yearling for the offering. Now follow me to the guest chamber and rest yourselves."

CHAPTER VII

GAMALIEL'S SCHOOL

Ben Gerber's shop was a busy place the next day. The old men gathered there to exchange with Azel the news from the different sections of the world. Saul spent the day in the streets.

Now that the great feast day was at hand and the hospitality of Jerusalem was extended, the pilgrims were becoming reasonable and kindly in their conduct toward one another. Knowing that he would see the Temple the next day, Saul spent his time in seeing the place of the Tombs of the Kings, and climbed to the hill whereon was built the palace of Herod. The modification of the architecture to suit the Roman idea did not seem to him as beautiful as that of Tarsus. He found the gymnasium in the Tyropoeon Valley which Herod had erected and which was shunned by the greater part of the Jews. He found the old walls of Nehemiah on the south side partly torn down and included with the newer walls. His fancy was inflamed with the recollection of the story of that great leader coming back and feverishly driving the people to activity in the rebuilding of the broken walls; and he almost dramatized himself as doing a like great work for his people.

When night came on the people in the streets crowded into every possible place to rest comfortably. Forbearance had taken the place of the fretfulness of the journey. The housetops were covered with weary slumberers who spread their own mats for their beds.

73

Even down in the courtyards, where there was any space not occupied by beasts of burden, men found a place to rest, and often the householder went there to sleep.

Before the break of day the city was awake. Food had been brought by most of the pilgrims, so that little preparation was necessary, and the inhabitants had made arrangements for this event long days before the time of the feast. In the dim light of the early morning men and women hastened to the Temple to attend the early service, but Ben Hanan decided to take Saul to Gamaliel. The grandfather resolutely set out for the Temple.

Gamaliel had a school which was simple in all its appointments, but famous among the Pharisees, commanding the respect of even the Sadducees, who bitterly resented the teachings in that school. In fact, the numerous controversies between the opposing sects were not deemed a full argument until the disputants had reached the stage where they could no longer express the intensity of their feelings by words, and resorted to spitting at one another. This unsanitary but common practice was deemed a fitting close to an earnest sectarian argument. In front of a plain house built against the walls of neighboring houses, with steps leading up to the door, flanked by Corinthian pilasters, and decorated with vines and grapes over the doorway like a synagogue, was a crowd of men so compact that it was almost impossible to pass among them to the door. They were gesticulating wildly, as was the manner of the people. The greater number wore the costume of white assumed by the Pharisees, but a few zealous Sadducees seemed delighted to find so many of the opposition at one place.

"Is this the school of Gamaliel?" Ben Hanan asked of a patriarchal Sadducee.

"Indeed it is," the Sadducee replied. "We came here to face some of the leading men who avoid answering us on the streets."

The doors of the school opened and the Pharisees went in. The Sadducees left, gloating that their opponents had not dared withstand their argument until the proper close of it. Ben Hanan led Saul into the room. The high ceiling and four pillars, one at each corner of the room, gave this school the appearance of a temple. Along the walls, below the high windows, were racks carrying bulky rolls of manuscript written on the thick sheets of parchment, and carefully protected rolls of papyrus. At the farther end of the room was a dais extending across the hall, on which rich rugs were spread, and on the floor of stone were thick, small rugs arranged in rows, on which the men were sitting. Gamaliel, in a spotlessly white robe, was seated on a rug on the dais. On each side of him were four other teachers, and all wore headdresses that betokened they were priests of the Temple. Ben Hanan spoke to a young Pharisee at the door and told him he wished to speak with Gamaliel.

Gamaliel rose, when the young man brought him the news, and went to meet Ben Hanan. At that time of his life Gamaliel was tall, and his well-kept, black, luxuriant beard, with a few streaks of white, seemed to glisten and ripple over his white robe. His rising was easy and full of dignity. His fine face and piercing eyes glowed with kindliness. While free from any effort at posing, yet his carriage was graceful and princely.

"I am Ben Hanan of Tarsus," said Saul's father, addressing Gamaliel. "This is my son, Saul, who has pursued his studies under Ben Arza to fit him as a rabbi. I bring him to establish him in your school, if such may be, to become a scholar. Whatever the charges and length of time required, provision will be made for him. It has been the purpose from his birth to place him under your teaching. Here are letters from Ben Arza."

"Let me read them," said Gamaliel, taking them and unrolling the record. He ran down over the list of items carefully set forth. He smiled, in a manly, winning way, and said:

"Ben Arza, with greater pains than I am used to seeing, has here set forth the time and record of your son, upon each division of the studies of the Law and the Prophets, giving a strong recommendation. We are about to examine others today for admission to this school. If you will leave him with us, we will soon decide."

Gamaliel, returning to the dais, told the assembled teachers who Saul was, spoke briefly of his family and the recommendations of Ben Arza. Ben Hanan, outside, leaning against one of the pilasters at the doorway, was so calm and rigid that passers-by hardly distinguished him from the structure. In this stern calm he waited for the decision.

The council of Gamaliel's school began examining Saul and making such frank comments that he was greatly embarrassed.

"How old are you?" asked Gamaliel in a wonderfully rounded, encouraging voice, just when the questions had become most disconcerting.

"Sixteen years," replied Saul, his confidence fully restored.

"Very small for his age," Jochanan, one of the teachers on the dais, commented.

"King Saul was head and shoulders above his fellows," Saul's eyes were flashing as he spoke, "and David was a small man; yet the Lord loved David."

Gamaliel smiled and the teachers about the room nodded to one another in approval.

"What trade would you learn?" Jochanan asked Saul.

"I am even now a tent-maker," Saul answered with pride, "and I know how to weave the cloth for making tents."

"He that has a trade in his hands," said Gamaliel to the teachers, "to what is he like? He is like a vineyard that is fenced."

The scribe, deeming this a good saying, immediately recorded it.

Then, on request of the teachers, who had now become friendly, Saul recited the laws, as a test of his preparation; and to his delight one asked him to give the law as to anyone persuading him to follow after strange gods.

"If a Gentile persuade you, what then?" Jochanan asked.

"A Gentile could not persuade a Pharisee," Saul retorted.

"Will the ten tribes return again?" one inquisitorial teacher asked.

"That I do not know," said Saul, "though Rabbi Ben Arza has told me that according to the traditions

they will not.   I hope to learn what traditions are worthy
of belief, if I may sit among you."

"It is not fair to question the lad on things we
debate," said Gamaliel. "Let the youth retire and
wait outside for our decision."

Saul, going to his father, told him that he was to
await the decision. Ben Hanan, with only a slight
change of his statuesque pose, seized Saul's hand and held
it so tightly while they waited that Saul winced.

"The personality and fitness of the applicant are now
open for discussion," said Gamaliel after Saul had left.

"While I am favorable to the lad," said Rabbi
Jochanan, the chief inquisitor, "yet I am bothered
about his size."

"You should have noticed with what erect and perfect
poise he stood the while of his examination, and how he
seemed to grow in stature when he spoke of Saul and
David," said Gamaliel. "You should have noted the
strong carriage of the lad; his supple muscles were
graceful in every movement, like the muscles of a mountain gazelle ready to lead in winged speed."

"I do not know if he will continue a student," said
one from the floor, "but those strange, heavy, meeting
eyebrows of his, in one so young, and the quick flash
of his eyes showing the power of a speaker, made me
wonder, after he had gone, if his answers were from
study or from mere power to divine the answer expected
by the question."

"I am glad you saw that," said Gamaliel. "All the
time the lad was before us I watched those expressive,
large eyes of his, flashing the energy of a mind, that,
seizing each question as if it were a swiftly flying mes-

senger out of a mysterious country on its way to an undiscovered land, instantly made it his captive. There is power in those eyes; beauty and strength of character are denoted by his nose; his thin, sensitive nostrils quivered like those of an Arab thoroughbred ready to dash into a race."

"We need not only brilliant minds," said Rabbi Surai, "but minds that will persist in the right, not the fickle ones who please for a little while; and I would have your opinion in that respect, O Gamaliel!"

"Had you followed him closely," Gamaliel said with fervor, "you would have seen that he clung closely to the ideas already fixed in his mind; and then his firm chin shows that he is prepared in his nature for persisting in his purpose. His fine, high head, long and thin, denotes a strong brain power, with great imagination. I liked the sweet tenderness of his lips, along with the firmness of his character. But let us now take the vote. Our scribe will prepare for the ballot."

The scribe rose with slips of parchment for the formal vote, and by a gesture Jochanan stopped him.

"Because of the love we have for our leader, Gamaliel, and because of the love he has for the lad," said Jochanan, "I am of the mind that the scribe should enter the lad's name without even a vote being taken, unless someone should wish to vote."

Immediately everyone was shouting, with upraised hand, "So be it!"

"The lad awaits your message," said Gamaliel to the scribe.

When the scribe made his announcement to Saul he added that the boy should come after the week of the

Passover. Ben Hanan, without releasing Saul's hand, bowed to the scribe and silently led Saul to Ben Gerber's house.

Martha, Ben Gerber, and Azel were impatiently waiting for Ben Hanan or Saul to tell the news; but Martha, reading in Saul's eyes the story, flung her arms around him.

"He is accepted by Gamaliel," said Ben Hanan very quietly.

"Was I not telling you," said the grandfather, rising from his rug in excitement, "how well he was schooled? He is a son of Kish."

Ben Hanan indulgently smiled at his father, then by his gesture all were seated on the rugs for a family conference.

"I have provided for his fees and clothes, but where should he lodge?" said Ben Hanan.

"That cannot be a question," said Ben Gerber, "for this is our house and he is our brother."

"If you will give me work and allow me the same wages you pay any other workman doing the same amount of work," said Saul with pride, "then I will pay my way with you, for my hands are skilled in your work."

"To have my brother under Gamaliel," said Martha, "is so much of an honor that I would gladly lodge him free."

"That is a gracious offer, Martha," said Ben Hanan, "but the boy is right, for Hillel himself has said, 'Study which is not combined with work must in the end be interrupted, and only brings sin with it.'"

"Let this be the understanding," said Ben Gerber. "Saul shall receive the same wages that I pay others for the same work, and he will live with us. Our food cost will be divided so that each shall pay his portion. Is that agreeable, Ben Hanan?"

"It is as Saul says," said Ben Hanan, waving his hand to Saul.

"It is so agreed," said Saul, reaching over and shaking hands in the Roman fashion with his brother-in-law, in token of closing the contract.

CHAPTER VIII

THE PASSOVER

After they had taken a short nap, as was the custom at midday, all the men started for the Temple to get the paschal lamb for that night. The old grandfather insisted that he would go with them. They ascended the stairway that led up to Herod's bridge, at the place on the western side of the Tyropoeon Valley where the way made a sharper ascent up the hill on which stood Herod's palace. This led them to the only western entrance of the Temple area, being on a level with the court of the Gentiles.

The Temple area occupied a space nearly 750 feet square, on the elevation of the eastern hill overlooking the city and almost as high as the western hill selected by Herod for his palace. The site of the Temple was on the very threshing-floor purchased by David, on which Solomon had erected his Temple and on which this Temple had been reconstructed by Herod. Entrance through the retaining walls by ramps led from the streets on the south side of the area into the outer court of the Gentiles. There were other entrances on the north side, and at the northwest corner of the high level space there loomed the tower of Antonia, overlooking the courts of the Temple.

Saul entered with the company through the western gate of the outer inclosure from the viaduct, and passed along the magnificent colonnade of four rows of 164 Corinthian columns, extending from east to west along the south wall, forming three aisles. The central aisle was 45 feet wide and the adjoining columns 100 feet high; each of the other aisles was 30 feet wide and the columns of the outside rows were 60 feet high. Beautifully carved beams of cedar covered the top of this colonnade. This was the unhindered expression of Herod's love of magnificence in reconstructing the Temple, and its courts. Though he had made it much larger than the old Temple of Solomon, it was only by holding to enlargements in nonessential parts that he was able to gain the co-operation of the Jews.

At the eastern end this colonnade was joined by a colonnade of three rows of pillars, running north and south along the eastern side of the area, with two walks or aisles; and the same kind of a colonnade was along the north wall. The entrance from this bridge on the west gave a vista of magnificence seldom equaled, and on coming into view of the eastern colonnade and part of the northern colonnade, the perspective gave an impression of bewildering distance, because of the symmetrical Corinthian columns under the great cedar beams resting on them. Even the angles at the eastern wall and the northern wall blended in the view, giving the impression that there was one continuous colonnade, merely turning gracefully in its endless course. The eye was so trained to grandeur by this vista, that upon turning to the massive, fortress-like walls surrounding the courts and the Temple proper, the high walls and higher towers at each of the eight entrances were in proper proportions.

The soreg, the terrace that surrounded the walls at the base on all sides of the fortress except the west, was

15 feet wide and was reached by a flight of fourteen steps at the eastern entrance, and a further flight of five steps led from the terrace to the wide east gate through a tower into the Women's Court. On the outer edge of the terrace was a stone balustrade 5 feet high, with tablets at the side of each entrance warning all Gentiles in Greek letters that they incurred the penalty of death if they passed beyond that limit. The outside dimensions of the immense, inclosing walls were 462 feet from east to west and 367 feet from north to south.

Ben Gerber led the way to the eastern gate, and Azel stopped the party.

"Let the wonderful view be impressed upon your memory, Saul," said the grandfather.

All stopped in admiration, more than that, in adoration. The nineteen steps in all led up to the landing on the level of the Women's Court; and at the farther side of that spacious court, open to the sky, was the ascent, by fifteen semicircular steps, to the entrance through another wall of the wide and high gate called the Gate Beautiful, or Nicanor's Gate. Still beyond the Gate Beautiful rose the massive altar of sacrifice, 47 feet square at the base, rising 25 feet by three reducing tiers, until the top was 32 feet square. The vista stretched farther and ended with the Temple proper, standing on a still higher platform, reached by a flight of twelve steps, in sections of four steps to a landing.

The Temple itself, polished marble, decorated with all of the art then known rose to a height of 150 feet above the platform level. In front of the Temple stood a screen supported by two beautiful columns ornamented with gold, and taking the places of the pillars Jachin and

Boaz, in the Temple built by Solomon. These pillars were 30 feet apart and the screen proper, composed of beams and stone work, extending across the tops of the pillars, was ornamented in bronze and gold with a massive grape vine, and bunches of grapes as large as a man.

Back of the screen was the opening into the vestibule of the Holy of Holies. The wide opening to the vestibule was without doors, but elaborate curtains shut out the view when the ritual did not provide for its use.

It was this scene, extending into a vista of terrace on terrace through spacious courts and wide doorways, reaching to the exquisite glory of the Temple itself, that held in trancelike adoration the attention of the old man exulting in its beauty, as well as the young man reveling in its magnificence.

After lingering long at the scene of grandeur they ascended to the soreg or first terrace, where they removed their sandals and placed them in their girdles, for no one wore shoes or sandals within the Temple; and, ascending the remaining five steps, they entered the Court of Women.

In this wide Court of Women was the great place of meeting. Around the sides and above the first stories were balconies, accommodating large numbers, and since few seats were provided, great crowds could gather. There were thirteen contribution boxes, cunningly formed as inverted ram's horns, in the court, to receive the contributions for Temple purposes, and this caused the court to be referred to also as the treasury. In the distance was the great doorway, 20 feet wide and 30 feet high, at the top of fifteen semicircular

steps, opening on the Court of Israel, a narrow space
set off by a railing from the large oblong space known as
the Priests' Court; the narrow space, the Court of
Israel, or Men's Court, extended around three sides
of the large oblong space in which was the massive
altar of sacrifice of uncut stone, with the incline up to
the south side.

Saul stopped in the Women's Court again to gaze
with amazement on the vista through the wide doors
to the altar of sacrifice and to the Temple in the distance.

Since applicants were admitted in groups of thirty
to receive their slaughtered lambs for the Passover,
it was a favor of the priest counting the number to permit
his friend Ben Gerber to take Saul with him into the
Men's Court as one of the group of thirty.

After a long wait, enjoyed by Saul in studying the
detail of the great inner Priest's Court, they were
admitted through a partition to an inclosure on the
north side of the altar of sacrifice. There the scene
changed from beauty to the drudgery of preparing for
the observance of the Passover. Lambs and cattle
were tied to the rings in the floor, waiting their use in
the religious ceremonies. It was a place of slaughter
as well as ceremony. The animals were slain, their
blood sprinkled on the corners of the altar, portions taken
for the sacrifice and (in the case of the paschal lamb)
the carcass cleaned and taken away by the person who
would use it for observance of the ancient eating of the
Passover. Now the slaughter took place in the Temple,
while in the past each family prepared the lamb to be
used.

During the afternoon the lamb was roasted in the home of Ben Gerber on spits of pomegranate wood, and all arrangements were made for the Passover. The guests who joined in celebrating the supper were in the house by the going down of the sun. The doors of the room were shut; men and women reclined on their left elbows on cushions around the large dining mat spread on the floor for the occasion. The men wore their sandals, their robes were gathered under their belts as if for a journey, and each had by his side his walking stick.

Ben Gerber, as host, pronounced the blessing on the first goblet of wine provided for each one, and it was drunk as a ceremony. Then a basin, a pitcher of water, and a napkin were carried around so that each participant, using a few drops of water, washed and wiped his hands, signifying his ceremonial cleanliness to participate in the supper.

After the ceremonial washing Ben Gerber called on Grandfather Azel to offer prayer. The old man arose stiffly, solemnly raising his hands almost though not quite level with his face, pronounced this benediction provided for the occasion:

"Blessed be Thou, the Eternal, our God, the King of the world, who has sanctified us by Thy commands, and hast ordained that we should eat the Passover."

Then the bitter herbs were handed around with some morsels of the unleavened bread. A second cup of wine was drunk after grace had been said. At this point Saul, representing the youngest male of the family, asked the question prescribed by custom:

"Why do we celebrate this day?"

"Now, who should tell the story?" said Ben Gerber in mocking doubt, while Azel, looking away, tried to appear indifferent but nervously plucked at his garment.

"Grandfather Azel is the only one to whom the honor belongs," said Martha.

"Of course," answered Ben Gerber, warmly, "I only asked the question to learn if anyone had any doubt. Azel will now tell the story."

In telling the story of the Hebrew children being led out of Egypt, and the night of the escape, the grandfather wove legends and comments into the account, permitted by custom, so that it was a running commentary on the revered traditions of the Passover. Azel put all the fervor of his ardent old age into the recital of the story—his voice and gestures were dramatic as he became lost to surroundings and transported to the inspiring theme of man in weakness stumblingly following the guidance of Jehovah.

The meal was partaken of, including, besides the lamb, bitter herbs and unleavened bread, a dish filled with a sop made of crushed dried fruits mixed with vinegar into which the bread was dipped. Azel asked Saul to recite Psalms 113 and 114, that part of the Hallel appropriate to the stage of the supper. Stirred by the recital, Saul put meaning into his intonation of the Psalms. The meal was finished, and a third cup of wine was served followed by a prayer. A fourth cup was served, followed by the benediction, and Saul recited the remainder of the Hallel, Psalms 115 to and including 118.

The remains of the lamb were placed on a fire that had been kept going to burn all that was left from the feast. All rose and, with Saul leading at the request of Ben Gerber, joined in chanting Psalm 136, sometimes called the "Great Hallel."

The hour was late. The men gave their cloaks another pull up under their girdles, picked up their staves as if about to set out on a long journey, and the guests departed. Ben Gerber and family went out with the guests as if they, too, would leave on the journey, but outside the door returned to their house.

CHAPTER IX

EARLY SERVICES

The next morning, being the Sabbath of the Passover, the multitude gathered for the early service in the Temple. While deep night was still on, a priest, who had been on the watch in the Temple, ceremoniously went to the chamber of priests, lifted a square stone, and took out a ponderous key. This he carried and gave to some sleeping Levites, who opened the great doors of the Temple.

Even at that early hour, the mass of people gathered was so great as to cover the spaces allotted to them. The priests and Levites aroused to sudden activity, and their ghostlike figures hastening in the dim light to their various duties, gave the great courts the appearance of a newly awakened hive of bees. The barefoot people moved about noiselessly.

The slumbering fires at the top of the great altar of sacrifices were renewed, the attendants brought up wood, others carried water to the basins used by the priests and to the tables on the north of the altar, where the sacrifices were prepared and cleansed. In solemn ritual a priest went from the altar of incense with a platter up the long incline of the altar of sacrifice and carried back live coals to start the fire on the altar of incense.

This being one of the great days, the people were permitted to enter the Priests' Court to within 18 feet of the Holy Place. Silently the crowd of worshipers were waiting for the ritual of the day.

There were priests and Levites assigned to every small thing to be done. An army of servers was present. While all priests would not be on duty at any one time, Josephus says that there were 2,500 priests authorized to serve in the Temple. The division of duties was such that at the altar of sacrifice a priest caught the blood of the sacrifice in a golden bowl and handed it to one of six priests in a row, who passed it from one to another until it reached the priest standing at the corner of the base of the altar, who handed the vessel to a priest carrying a bundle of reeds like a small broom, with which he sprinkled the blood on each side of the corner of the altar. Meanwhile, the ones who offered the sacrifice, either in person or one for several, symbolically touched the sacrifice with his hand.

Before the morning light the family of Ben Gerber and his guests had gathered in the Temple for the Sabbath of the Passover. Azel, wearied from his journey and the excitement of his devout attendance at the Temple, was present, notwithstanding the fact that his sleep had been cut short by the supper of the night before. The great whiteness of the Holy Place loomed in the faint light of the night, as if it were supporting the heavens.

With his keen eyes Saul was watching a priest walking along the top of the north wall, silhouetted against the misty half-light of the sky. The priest disappeared in the tower over one of the gates and shortly reappeared at the very top of the tower. He stood so still that he looked as if he were a statue. Saul saw the priests gathering just within the Holy Place, at the altar of incense, on which the fire was lighted, and with the lamps

of the golden candlestick relighted revealing Levites
standing by with rams' horns. One priest fed the fire
with small sticks of wood, another stood by with an
elaborately decorated jar of incense and a silver ladle.
Out in front of them stood the high priest, this being
one of the great days he officiated, in all the glory of
the white, purple, scarlet, and gold of his jeweled robes
of office, silently watching the statuesque figure on top
of the tower. While the time was long, the intense
stillness made it seem longer. Now the crowd had
become so compact that it would seem impossible for
them to kneel in the service.

Out of the stillness of the night now graying into dawn
there came a high-pitched cry from the priest on the
tower, "Barkai!" (the morning light has appeared).

"Has the light in the east reached Hebron?" came
in a rich, sonorous chant from the chief officer of the
Temple beside the high priest at the altar of incense.

"It has," responded the watchman on the tower
in the same high-pitched voice.

"Go and fetch a lamb from the chamber of lambs,"
said the high priest in his deep chant.

Then followed a pause while the sunrise poured in
the first bright tints of dawn. The fire on the altar of
incense blazed brighter, the priest with the jar poured
the incense from the ladle on the fire and the smoke
circled in a high column. The fragrance of the incense
was settling over the people. The Levites sounded
three blasts on their horns. Crowded as they were,
the worshipers found space to kneel, bowing their heads
to the floor. Shortly again there were three blasts;

the people rose. The flames leaped up from the altar of sacrifice; and the priests were going up the long incline with the lamb for the sacrifice of the day.

Again three blasts sounded from the horns. The Levites began reciting the greater Hallel because this was the great day. One company of Levites would recite a line in a high-keyed chant and then another company of Levites would recite a line in a deep melodious chant; the men with horns would keep in time, as well as fill the space between responses; and there were women with long, silvered trumpets who joined in the intonation of the chants. The people joined in, swelling the chorus until it resounded out over the city, and echoed along the valleys of the Kidron and Hinnom.

The morning sun, well up in the sky, revealed the façade of the Holy Place in all its splendor. The two columns of the screen and the gold-embellished crossbeams were fiery gold. The curtains to the Holy Place were pulled back on this festal day, so that the people might see the interior of the vestibule with its three pieces of furniture, the altar of incense, the stand of seven golden candlesticks, and the table of shewbread; its high ceiling, augmented by a painting of the firmament, its side walls decorated in subdued colors with symbols of deity, the wings of power. At the back of the vestibule the two parts of the great, heavy, purple curtains, 3 inches thick, in the weaving and dyeing of which the priest-workman had given attention to every thread, were drawn aside, their rich folds framing the massive, carved, and inlaid doors of the Holy of Holies.

The Holy of Holies, in the ancient Temple the place
of the Presence, the Ark of the Covenant, and the Tables
of the Law, now merely a vacant room, was a perfect
cube of 20 cubits, but still venerated as a most sacred
memorial of all its revered associations. Because of
their enthusiasm the people in this Presence felt no
weariness.

CHAPTER X

AZEL'S VISION

After the morning services Ben Gerber, noticing that Azel looked very worn, urged the old gentleman to forego the sacrifice that was to be offered by Ben Hanan, and return to the house for rest.

"What madness has come upon you, Ben Gerber," cried the old man in mingled anger and grief, "that you would prevent me from this last sacrifice, and to be with Saul in his first?"

Waiting their turn the company of Ben Hanan, with Ben Gerber's family, finally entered the place of sacrifice north of the altar, where they had received the paschal lamb the day before. Many animals, to be used as sacrifices, were tied to the rings in the floor. Ben Gerber pointed out the one he had purchased days before from a farmer; and the priest, after taking a slip of identification from Ben Gerber, had the fat, sleek yearling male calf brought forward. Its front feet were tied to its hind feet, it was thrown on its side with its head toward the south, face toward the west. The priest drew a knife of special kind for sacrifice; another priest was ready with the gold basin to catch the blood. Azel with Saul touched the animal, while the rest knelt. The priests near at hand were repeating the shorter Hallel. The priest gave a particular stroke with the knife, the blood was sprinkled on the corner of the altar after being passed up by the six intermediate priests. Every detail was governed by regulation.

Grandfather Azel rose with joy in his face that he had participated in this ritual, so full of deep meaning to him—a renewed covenant between him and Jehovah, a dedication of his grandson to the life of a teacher, a cleansing of his conscience that Jehovah had heard and forgiven him, a supreme joy that once more, perhaps for the last time, he had faithfully complied with the Law of Moses. The Temple Beautiful dazzled his eyes and then seemed to float away with the silvery clouds in the blue dome.

Ben Hanan had been watching his father closely and sprang in time to catch him as he fell.

They bore the grandfather out of the Temple and down to the home, where he tossed in fever throughout the day and night. All night long Saul had sat by his grandfather, who would call for him if he were absent. Saul had tenderly raised his grandfather's head often during the night to give him a sup of water. The morning light was just stealing through the latticed windows. Ben Hanan had come in and was sitting on the other side of the grandfather's mat, listening with troubled brow to the heavy breathing of the old man. Suddenly Azel opened his eyes, burning brightly from the fever. He looked and saw his grandson, then turning to Ben Hanan he gazed fixedly upon him.

"Deal kindly with the lad," the old man gasped, "for he is a true son of Kish. Lay me away beside the road coming into the Damascus Gate, so that in the resurrection I may join the host coming back to the Temple."

With great effort the old man raised himself on his right elbow, placed his hand on Saul's head, and seemed unable to say anything for a while.

"Look you, Saul," the old man cried after a long silence, pointing to the window through which the sunlight was pouring, "there it is, eternal in the heavens. I lost sight of the Temple while at the sacrifice; but there—there it is, now, translated to the skies! Great is the Lord our God!"

He fell back, gasped a few times, then his breath gently left his body. In a long stillness sat Ben Hanan; then, bowing his head in his hands, he sobbed the great sobs of a strong man giving over to his grief.

Saul did not move for a long time. He felt that he was sitting beside a prophet of old. At last he yielded to the knowledge of his loss and, throwing himself upon the bosom of the old man, wept bitterly.

CHAPTER XI

AT GAMALIEL'S FEET

After the burial of Grandfather Azel and the week of mourning had been observed, Ben Hanan bade Saul farewell. For the whole of a long day Saul sat in the upper chamber of Ben Gerber's house in deep meditation. He was brave enough to endure the separation from his family; he felt that the loss of his grandfather was inevitable; and, while he mourned his death, Saul did not feel it was a cause for unreasonable grief. In the great confidences of the home life Azel had told him of the joy he expected, if he served his time faithfully in the body. For a while he thought of Tabitha, but he turned from that subject with a firm resolve that it should wait its time. He was thinking of the impressions he had received from all this new life and the new scenes; what would be his place in the affairs of life; what would be his goal. Vaguely he knew that he would be a rabbi, but what should he do to discharge the duties of such office so as to accomplish any great purpose?

His mind followed in winding detail the scheme that would take him back to his home as a teacher of men, and vainly he tried to think of a method to present the Jewish religion in an attractive way. He communed with himself, and then concluded that faith was the only safe reliance; all else was the caprice of surroundings. It was not an idle waste of time. He was obeying the great impulse of his nature in thinking for himself.

When he reported to the school of Gamaliel he was placed with boys about his own age. In a few days the teacher to whom he had been assigned reported to Gamaliel that Saul was only being held back by the boys in that class and that he should be placed in a more advanced class. He made rapid progress under the new teacher, or, at least, so it seemed to the teacher, but Saul was earnestly hoping that he would soon come to some study that was new to him. Gamaliel would drop in on the class once in a while and his practiced eye saw that the drudgery of reviewing the things with which he was familiar would kill off Saul's ambition. Thus it came about that Gamaliel took Saul as a special scholar and gave him a place in his own study.

In Gamaliel's library Saul found the writings of Plato and Aristotle, some of the *Dialogues* of Socrates, and wonderfully interesting letters from Philo and other teachers in Alexandria. He found many of the Roman laws and his mind was quick to grasp them.

In the conversations with his favored pupils Gamaliel showed the broad mind for which he was famous. In these conversations Saul learned the simplicity and depth of other great minds; the tests to be applied to find out if a man were sincere in his arguments; to distinguish between the man who simply aped the learned and the man who sincerely assimilated knowledge and desired to impart it to others. These close associations with Gamaliel also brought Saul into the discussions among other learned men and especially in close connection with the members of the Sanhedrin or Jewish senate, of which there were two divisions: the lesser or local Sanhedrins, composed of twenty-three members, and the one greater Sanhedrin, composed of seventy-one members, over which the high priest presided.

Long before Saul's time a class of men known as the learned or the scribes, disassociated from priestly orders, had devoted themselves to the study and interpretation of the written law as found in the Torah or Pentateuch, and the traditions or the unwritten law of customs called the Halacha. The Pharisees held the Halacha to be equally authentic and binding with the Torah, but not superseding it, merely explaining the application of the general provisions of the written law, and the Sadducees denied any authority to the law of customs.

Back in the Maccabean time, the leaders or the notables, closely associated with the government, were from the priestly orders and were accused of neglecting strict observance of the law because engrossed with political affairs, and they resented any such belief as the Pharisees held because it would embarrass their freedom in wars, politics, and dealings with other nations. While the original cause of difference had disappeared to a considerable extent, yet the animosity between the two divisions had continued and the difference as to the authority of the unwritten law continued. A marked difference, arising primarily over the acceptance or refusal to accept the unwritten law, was that the Pharisees affirmed a resurrection of the dead, and the Sadducees denied it.

Herod the Great deprived the Pharisees of the power they had gained in the Sanhedrin by the simple expedient of killing off a large number who were members of that body and appointing others. At one time there had been open war between the sects and many were slain.

The scribes, through all the changes, had devoted themselves to the study of the Torah and the Halacha to find from the two sources an interpretation that would govern in every detail the lives of the individuals and all the services of the Temple. While the Torah was so sacred that no word of it could be changed and while its terms were often general, yet the scribes held that it was the supreme law and that it must be applied to every detail and that this could only be accomplished by resort to the law of customs, the Halacha. The law of customs was written out long after Saul's time and is said to be included in the Mishna.

There were many who insisted that the law of customs had been given by Moses and handed down from mouth to ear through the generations. While no word of the Halacha could be written, yet no word of it could be varied. The scribes who received the unwritten law had been selected for their skilled and accurate memories, even the Hebrew word meaning "to teach" was the same as "to repeat."

From the time of Hillel, the grandfather of Gamaliel, the influence of the Pharisees, from whom came the great body of scribes, increased in the Sanhedrin. A scribe's judgment had all the weight of a judge's decision among the people. Not only were the scribes selected from among devout men but every teacher enjoined upon them the strictest observance of all the laws. They were held in high esteem by the people, for the people liked to have such rules as would keep them distinct from other nations.

Those who were active in the studies of the law gathered in schools such as Gamaliel conducted, meeting at times in the court of the pillars, or the court of the Gentiles adjoining the Temple for discussions. While they sought to find a rule for every action and condition tending to a more complete observance of the Torah, they were zealously deducing rules that would keep the Jews separate from the Gentiles, and when adopted by the Sanhedrin these rules of separation affected the Jews of the Dispersion who were liable to become Hellenized in their far-off adopted countries.

Saul was busily occupied during this period of his life, for he had rapidly advanced in scribism under Gamaliel until he was taking part in the discussions besides learning the unwritten law. He was at work during the early morning hours in Ben Gerber's shop, and in the school among the scribes from the middle of the forenoon until past midday. It was seldom that he had all his remaining part of the afternoon from the shop, but he managed to attend the gymnasium some of the time in order to build his strength while yet a young man. In his eagerness to gain all advantages to be had from the gymnasium he was known as the most enthusiastic among those taking exercises there.

In the freedom of discussion permitted in the school of Gamaliel, a scribe older than Saul proposed a question to Gamaliel whether or not it was a violation of the law for a Jew to participate with Gentiles in athletics.

"I have noticed that our young brother Saul," said the scribe, "often goes to the gymnasium built by Herod."

"How find you the directors there as compared with those in Tarsus?" Gamaliel good-humoredly asked.

"They are not as careful, and they have little regard for the purity of athletics," said Saul.

"I contend," said the older scribe, "that it is contaminating for a Jew to attend these heathenish places. It leads to familiarity with their statues and idols."

"I do not agree with you," said Gamaliel. "I often go to the public bath, in which one of the decorations is a statue of Venus, and I feel no contamination. The statue was put there for ornament and the bath was not constructed for the statue."

Saul centered on the constant interpretations and repetitions of the traditions until he mentally revolted against the system of endless deductions of rules of conduct daily engaging the sittings of the scribes. The reverence demanded by all teachers from their pupils and the respect Gamaliel evoked without appealing to any rule of conduct raised a barrier to Saul making any protest to his teacher. He thought that it was only within his own soul that conflict was known.

Gamaliel had asked Saul, in a casual way, to search the manuscripts for any common ground or common thought between the Greek philosophers first as among themselves, and next with the Jews. Saul having made the search laid his conclusions before his teacher.

"You will note," said Gamaliel, "that the thinkers of every age among all people seek the origin of life with the idea that from this origin flows the supreme law of goodness. Either tediously or fantastically they arrive at a conclusion. It has seemed to me that each thinker for himself has received a revelation, more or less instructive according to the zeal with which he sought knowledge, that gave a high conception of the destiny of man—linking him with immortality."

"My soul is weary and I am strangely disturbed," said Saul. "I do not doubt, but I wonder why all this toil of the scribes to find a more exacting means of observing the law to appease God."

"Your doubts have been known to me for many days," said Gamaliel, speaking with that sympathetic understanding that made Saul from that instant a hero worshiper. "In the first place, there comes into every man's life a period of doubt, likely due to physical development, the transition from youth to fixed manhood. Happy is the man who comes through strong and clean. In the next place, you are at the stage of mental development where you are tempted to abandon early training and to take up new ideals. This is critical, lest impulse drive you so far that you will lose the way of your life."

"I heed the warning, O Gamaliel," said Saul as if the kindly sympathy of his teacher had refreshed him, "but now for the question that disturbs me, Why does the Law demand of the Jews such rigid ceremonial life?"

"I cannot answer that question fully," said Gamaliel, "for it involves more knowledge of Jehovah's plans than it has been possible for me to obtain. There are many sufficient reasons; chiefest is that by this plan Jews have a consciousness of doing the things that will please God. Other philosophies speculate upon the attributes of God, and what are the virtues men should imitate, but such speculation fails to establish the close relationship that the observance of laws has fixed between our daily life and Jehovah—the very narrowness of Jews has saved

to them through the centuries the high thought that
Jehovah is the origin of all things. With the authority
given me as a teacher I have used the ineffable name,
Jehovah."

"My dear teacher," said Saul, "now that my soul
is naked before you, I confess a desire to know more
than the mere repetition of the Halacha."

"The very impulse that has given us prophets,"
said Gamaliel. "You should now give part of your time
to the study of the history and the prophets, the edify-
ing Scriptures, the Haggada—field of fruits and flowers
that surrounds the stone wall Halacha. That fervid
imagination of yours should develop in Haggada so that
you can give to our people the poetry and imagery necessary to their sentimental natures; but I charge you
not to condone any failure or refusal to observe the law,
nor any abatement of it—no, not one jot or tittle, whether
it be the written law, or the law by tradition."

"Will that not lead me to the same view as is held
by the Sadducees, save that you include the Halacha?"
Saul asked earnestly.

"Not so long as we have our schools," said Gamaliel.
"It is the business of the scribes to search the Scriptures,
to apply the law of custom to the interpretation of the
Torah so that the law keeps up with changing conditions,
and when the real meaning has been found, we secure the
approval of the Sanhedrin and it then becomes binding
upon the priesthood as well as on the people. A rabbi
and scribe must retain everything he has received just
as he has received it and so impart it, and his life must
exemplify the things he teaches so that no shame shall
come upon the Word—as a goodly lined cistern retains

every drop of water emptied into it, so the worthy scribe retains every word as it was given to him."

Under the inspiration of Gamaliel, Saul applied himself to study with renewed interest. This searching for the right and wrong, or casuistry, made the work of the scribes endless, and laid many burdens of observance on the people. The scribes had extended many of the laws so that the priests of the Temple received more for their support, causing some grumbling among the people.

As a strict Pharisee Saul wore the white robe with blue fringe affected by his sect. Also he wore, especially when in or about the Temple and often on the streets, the phylacteries affected by the scribes and Pharisees. The phylacteries were small, square boxes opening like a locket, one worn on the inside of the left forearm and one was worn on the forehead, and they contained on parchment four passages from the Torah—Exodus 13: 1-10, 11-16; Deuteronomy 6:4-9; and Deuteronomy 9:13-21—all on one slip in the case on the arm, but on separate slips in the case on the forehead. The one on the arm was fastened by two straps wound seven times around the arm and three times around the hand, and the one on the forehead was fastened with straps hanging down in a prescribed way, and sometimes fastened with a decorated fillet.

Saul found that the rigid rules applied to the Halacha did not apply to the historical and prophetical parts of the Torah. The body of legends and traditions associated with the non-legal Scriptures was known as the Haggada, and the term included the method of interpretation. While the teaching of the Halacha was concerned with

carrying into effect every part of the written law, and
extending the law to every new condition, on the other
hand, the Haggada, the sayings, gave free scope to the
imagination, invested the recorded history with supple-
mental stories explaining motives and reasons, casting
the glamor of romance and imagery around even the
dry precepts of the law, released the imagination, and
gave enough freedom to fancy to satisfy the avid senti-
mentalism of the oriental.

It was in this part of his study that Saul learned the
legends and acquired the style of weaving about the text
new combinations characteristic in his later life in making
his appeals to mixed peoples, such as his reference to
the legend of the magicians, Jannes and Jambres, opposing Moses, or to the legend of the rock that gave water
to the wanderers, following them in the wilderness.

The two lines of thought represented by the Halacha
and the Haggada went along together and constituted
the equipment of any man worthy of being a scribe.

While giving much of his time to study and preparation Saul came in contact with the practical life of the
people through prevalent complaints and the discussion
among the scribes of the changes in conditions and what
would be necessary to meet the changes. The scribes
had taught the segregation of the Jews both in their
eating and in their marriage relations with the idea of
making the lives more acceptable to Jehovah.

The taxes exacted by Rome became symbols to the
Jews of acknowledgment of a heathen religion; the tax-
gatherers were cordially hated. The complaints of the
people against Rome embarrassed the leaders, because
they were powerless against the government which estab-

lished law and tranquility. To add to the embarrassment of the leaders among the scribes, an organization called the Zealots, composed of fanatics and desperate men having nothing in common with the scribes, fomented rebellion and caused uprisings against officers of the government, claiming that they were following the teachings of the scribes and Pharisees.

In this distraught condition Saul's early training in Tarsus gave him a broader view of affairs. He was judicial when others were excited, he was loyal to Rome while others only had hate for the Empire. He was tolerant of the messianic Haggada prevailing, but insisted on Jews developing their own religious life under the freedom granted by Rome. The many questions developed in Saul his latent qualities of statesmanship.

While on his way one day to meet other scribes in the court of the Gentiles for a discussion, Saul stopped at the school to leave word where he was going. He learned that Philo of Alexandria would visit Gamaliel that day.

"Stay, my son," said Gamaliel to Saul, "and meet this interesting scholar."

Philo came in shortly, his kindly face showing the lines of one who had thought deeply. He had the bearing of a man with a message worth hearing.

"I have turned aside from my journey to Ephesus," said Philo, the great haggadist, to the assembled school, "to meet my respected friend and fellow-laborer, Gamaliel; and I take this opportunity to congratulate you on having so devout and so advanced a teacher. It is my pleasure to find in him a co-worker in the interesting field of sorting out the fundamental things among the great teachers and philosophers of Greece and comparing them with the basic teachings of Moses. There is a vast deal of help found in the study of ancient teachings in Egypt. I believe I will be able to convince eminent Greeks that the correct understanding of the Logos is the foundation of unity of belief in the Supreme Being, and that idea once established will constitute an easy approach to the universal knowledge of Jehovah; for all men instinctively look for the first cause, the beginning."

The time passed rapidly, for Philo's words were refreshing and inspiring. He brought a new idea of universal love in his story; he said teachers should bring men of all nations first to the comprehension of God as Spirit, and that then would be the proper time to win them to the accepted form of worship.

CHAPTER XII

ACCEPTING RESPONSIBILITY

At the end of two years Ben Hanan again visited Jerusalem, and now treated Saul with much more consideration. He was pleased to find Saul associated with prominent scribes; he spent a long time with Gamaliel, who urged that Saul should become a permanent resident of Jerusalem, because of his fitness and his influence.

"Our world centers in Tarsus," said Ben Hanan. "There are now half-a-million people in our city, and no one has been fitted to cope with the teachings of the Greeks or with the lax morals brought us from Rome. His work lies where it is most needed."

"At least," said Gamaliel, "I hope for the time that he may become a member of the Greater Sanhedrin. If he grows in judgment, and if he becomes the head of his own family, I will be glad to stand sponsor for him as a member from Cilicia."

"I pray that I may not become vain," said Ben Hanan, humbly. "My greatest wish would then be realized."

Saul was growing, not tall, but sturdy. His face had filled out along character lines that Gamaliel had noticed in the boy, and the young man's beard gave him the air of the added strength of well-timed maturity.

It was at this visit of Ben Hanan that Martha's latest-born was named Ahiram, according to the Jewish rites, and Saul assisted at the ceremony. So attached to the child did Saul become that the little fellow tried

to cling to Saul two years later when the young rabbi
left for his home in Tarsus, and Saul loved the child as
if it were his own.

Not only was Saul prepared by study of the law, by
service in the Temple, and a general knowledge of other
philosophies but he was compelled to take a thorough
course in the knowledge of diseases, their cure and
prevention. He knew not alone the remedies, but how
to prepare them, mostly from herbs; and he was versed
in all the well-known means of caring for the sick and
disabled. As a rabbi he had to have this knowledge, in
order to teach those youths who would never have the
chance to come to Jerusalem to study, as well as to discharge the duties of relief and visitation imposed on a rabbi.

In many of the synagogues there were men who could
read the ancient Hebrew and translate it into the Aramaic, the language used by the Jews of Palestine and
by nearly all Jews in addition to the Greek.   The Hebrew
was at that time a dead language. Saul so fitted himself that he could do his own translating and would not
have the need of a translator, usually provided for the
leader of the Sabbath-day services.

The recital of all the preparation of a rabbi who was
sent out from Gamaliel's school may seem almost endless,
but infinite care was necessary to secure and maintain
the reputation of Gamaliel, who in turn maintained the
reputation of his great predecessor, Hillel, who had said:
"He who engages in business cannot become a sage;
and in a place where there are no men, strive thou to be
a man."

In four years Saul had covered all the courses laid
down for five years, and he was pointed to as one worthy

of emulation in study. He had arrived at man's estate, a young man of twenty sitting in the council with men of ripe years. His tact, his wide knowledge of men, his naturally kindly disposition, his flaming zeal when aroused, his uncompromising regard for truth had won him a place in the esteem of all he met.

He had been set apart as a rabbi in formal ceremonies, both by the school of Gamaliel and the Cilician synagogue which he attended, and where at times he conducted the services or gave the discourse of the day.

The great number of synagogues in Jerusalem at this time—there being over four hundred—was a curious commentary on the devotion of a people complaining of heavy taxation both by the Roman government and by the Temple, for every synagogue had to be supported, although it was merely a place of assembly for the particular class of people who found congenial associates in the one they selected.

The Great Sanhedrin had been a place of wonderful experience for Saul. He often sat in the outer circle of scribes, just outside the semicircle of members, and listened to the debates on questions of great importance, as well as heated controversies over mere details; and sometimes he had been called to fill temporarily the place of some absent member.

It was the highest judicial and legislative body of the Jews; though deprived of much authority without the assent of the representative of the Roman government, it had unlimited power concerning religious matters or matters pertaining wholly to Jewish law. While the Sanhedrin was always identified with the Temple by having the high priest as its president, yet in filling vacancies many Pharisees had been selected because of their eminence in the study of the law. At times the body had been made up at the direction of the representative of the ruling power assuming the authority to do so, but this occurred only rarely in history. It was a self-perpetuating body, and among the qualifications for membership in it was that the candidate should be the head of a family and have children of his own.

Saul had become so interested in his work that he regretted the approach of the time that he must leave, especially did he regret the separation from his young nephew, Ahiram, for between them a warm attachment had grown up. In anticipation of leaving by the sea for Tarsus, Saul had gathered quaint little presents for the members of his family, and recklessly he invested in an expensive necklace of Egyptian design as a gift to Tabitha.

"You are now a man among men," said Gamaliel to Saul, whom he had summoned to a conference. "A strange mission, for which you are fitted, has been placed in my hands to fill. Flavius Gratus, the proconsul, who is now in the city, has received word from Damascus that certain Jews of this city are stirring up an insurrection in Damascus; and the powers in Rome have sent word that he shall send someone to whom the Jews will listen, to quell the rebellious spirit by persuasion before it bursts into activity."

"But I am too young a man to intrust with such an important mission as this," Saul urged.

"I would not send you, if I did not think your ability and talents were equal to the occasion," replied Gamaliel.

"Tell me, Saul, are you in a hurry to return to Tarsus to make some maiden your wife?"

"Such thought did not make me so answer," Saul spoke frankly, but with a flush that told his hopes. "I have not the promise of anyone, but still I doubt my ability for this errand."

"Go," Gamaliel said with great earnestness, "and the success of your efforts there will give me the grounds for urging your name before the Sanhedrin, if it so be that your eloquence wins in Tarsus. Besides, you should be able to compare the beauty of Damascus with your home land. Let us go to the proconsul and get the information. I have told him that your loyalty to Rome is unquestioned."

"But I cannot enter the service of Rome," Saul urged, as if doubting the judgment of Gamaliel.

"Do not so consider it," said Gamaliel. "The expenses and sending you are entirely my concern. I want to save the people from their own folly and for the time that they will become so strong in faith that the righteousness of their cause will prevail. This is not for Rome. It is for our own people, and the calamity must be avoided in spite of our own people."

"I will go," said Saul with resolution.

CHAPTER XIII

FACING OPPOSITION

In the audience with Flavius Gratus, Saul learned that it was the governor's desire to prevent an uprising in Damascus by the Jews; in fact, that he was in strong sympathy with the Jews; that if the trouble started in Damascus, it would be largely due to agitators who had gone from Jerusalem, and, when the matter would be thoroughly sifted, he feared the word would come from the emperor to suppress all activities of Jews and deny them the privileges now given them.

Saul went from this interview to the Men's Court on the south side of the altar of sacrifice, opposite the inclined approach to it. He was alone. This place had become sacred to him as a place of devotion. The fires of the altar and the officiating priest were in full view in front, and to his left rose the marble front of the Temple. He felt that all this magnificence was an effort to express the adoration of the individual man for Jehovah. He knew that his days of preparation were over; that he was to plunge into a mission that was most difficult; and that he was at one of the turning-points in his life. He needed help beyond the counsel of man to give.

Prayer has been defined most successfully by devout writers; it has been prescribed by every ritual of religious organizations among idol and Christian worshipers; it has been encouraged by teachers of morals; it has been ridiculed by the cynics of every generation in the centuries of man; it is laughed at by the thoughtless; and yet it remains the sacred and exalted communion of the souls of great men and of the great souls of common men with the Infinite. It may not change the laws of nature, it may not turn aside disaster, but it fills the heart of the devotee with courage and gives him that sense of freedom from fear by which he carries on to the end of his course.

In devotion Saul prayed long and earnestly. He rose from his posture with his resolution confirmed to go on and meet the problems of his life in confidence. His mind was clear of any doubts; his soul had made a compact with the Supreme Being; he was above the annoyances and criticisms of jealous or short-sighted men; his vow was with the Most High. This was his dedication.

The arrangements were hastily made, including letters of credit which would enable Saul to secure animals for transportation. He bade his friends and relatives farewell. He followed the upper road and came into the Damascus road at the upper end of the Sea of Galilee. There he crossed the Jordan and climbed the hills to the east. He left Caesarea Philippi and Mount Hermon to his left. The way was long and tedious, taking him at least eight days to reach Damascus. On the high plateau, long before he reached the city, he could see the course of the river Abana, marked by the growth of trees. The peaks of the Lebanon Mountains seemed, through the clear air, to march with and hover over him. Little, yellow, round hills lay on the right, marking off the desert of the east. In a cloudless sky the sun swung on its fiery way, as if it would burn the rocks that lay along the roadway. Slowly, so slowly that it seemed at times there was no progress, slowly, Saul pushed on his way. Then there shot up out of the distance the poplar trees, the palms, the housetops, the walls of Damascus.

Coming into the oasis, he found the waters of the Abana distributed through many channels hidden by fruit and almond trees, and a riot of verdure. The great street of columns stretched away into the distance, suddenly checked by the desert that drank up the abundance of water sent rushing from the snowy Lebanon Mountains.

With his introductions Saul soon had a meeting of the leaders of the Jews, and told them of the great love the people of Jerusalem had for their kindred scattered through many cities. He told them of his native city of Tarsus, its great history, but not as old as Damascus; of the wanderings of the Hebrews from the days of Abraham and how Abraham no doubt passed through this very place to the land he sought to make his own. Then he reminded them of the faith of Abraham and of the promises Jehovah had made him.

"Are the promises of God to be doubted? Have you lost faith in those promises?" Saul asked them.

"We are faithful to the Lord our God. Why question us?" cried out Hyrcanus, one of the leaders of the revolting section.

"For this reason:" said Saul with such suddenness that replies were not ready, "We learn in Jerusalem that in your madness you would rise against the superior power of Rome with force of arms, when you are so puny that one legion of the countless legions of Rome would destroy you as mere brawlers.

"Aye, more than that, you would bring your brethren in Jerusalem to degradation; our Temple would be taken from us; our brethren in distant cities would be made to suffer for your madness; the privileges of worship which we have now would be taken from us; our captivity would be worse than the captivity of our fathers. Have you lost faith in the promises made to us? We are to be a mighty nation only if we obey God. Concern yourselves with your own duties; make your lives above reproach; live the law. Join with all Jews in obedience, and thus we will grow strong and the Lord will make clear the day of our deliverance. Hush every voice that persuades you to follow after the ways of futile revolution. Bear the burdens, however grievous, as those who have the assurance of the Most High God that you are his people."

Immediately, the agitators began their cries to put him out of the synagogue, but he stood before them in silence, with such dignity that none dared lay hand upon him. After the first tumult had subsided, leading men, merchants, and rabbis took up the argument on the side of Saul. It was late in the night before the arguments ceased.

"I must not leave until I am able to send word to the revered Gamaliel that all is well," said Saul. "And since he knows who are the leaders among you, as well as those who have come up here to stir you up, I can only give him the assurance which he must have to stay the hand of Rome by having the solemn pledge of these men that they will cease and will live orderly. That word must be evidenced by writing, so that if violated, Gamaliel may hand to the Roman authorities the names of the men responsible."

Again there was an uproar, but after much discussion the written pledge was given to Saul to send to Gamaliel.

Saul took the northern trade route over the mountains and was compelled to turn aside to Antioch to get animals to carry him on to Tarsus. During his brief stay in Antioch he visited the Gardens of Daphne built by Herod, and saw the beauty and the madness of the great pleasure resort. Money had not been spared to make the hills and grottoes rival the seductive sensualism of dream and fable. There he found dissipation unrestrained and pleasure expressed by depravity. The Greek art which he admired was here made coarse and common by its association with unbridled passion. And with all the vulgarity, Saul was touched with the beauty and grace of architecture and design: the vales had been made into bowers of blossoms and leaves; the miniature lakes nestled at the foot of hills covered with tamarisk bending to the slightest breeze; fountains gushed out of shaded rocks; bronze figures, lewd yet graceful—the artistic appreciation of Saul eliminated the grotesque and vulgar. The great street, lined with columns as far as the eye could reach, was, after all, only a way leading men not to think.

Impatiently he made his way around the gulf, a distance of 100 miles. The last day he was so eager that he would not stop for the usual noonday rest, but urged his tired animals on, against the protest of the owner. Late in the evening he entered his beloved Tarsus, after an absence of four years.

PART III

A Rabbi in Tarsus

CHAPTER XIV

THE FAMILY CIRCLE

Saul, the youth, had left Tarsus in the early morning; Saul, the man, returned in the shadows of the evening. He was weary, travel-stained; the day and hour of his arrival were not known to his family. His entry into the city led him through the upper part, unchanged, and yet strange to him. The streets, the houses, the school of Nestor, the arena, the palace of the governor, to his eyes, inflamed from the burning light of the road, were twisting and floating in the grotesquely changing proportions of a mirage. The booths were empty along the tradesmen's streets, the doors were closed, the streets were almost forsaken. Through the latticed upper windows lights were showing. The scenes were familiar to him, but it was the familiarity of boyish memory; and now the weary man tried to adjust all the details back into their proper places, along with his knowledge of other cities.

He had seen Damascus, the queen of the desert; of course, Jerusalem was indelibly fixed in his mind; he had recently beheld the pomp and shame of Antioch, with its pleasure resort. He felt that Tarsus was just as he had left it, but the thrill of its greatness was not what his fancy, feeding on loyal memory, had anticipated; or, rather, other scenes now claimed a place for comparison; and still it was his beloved Tarsus.

Dismounting and settling with his companion from Antioch, he made his way with a heavy heart through

the booth to the door of the shop. The years had
slipped away from him in the short time of his heavi-
ness of spirit. He was once more the lad waiting
for the door to open. Repeated knocking brought
Ben Hanan, bearing a lamp, to open the door. Seeing
it was Saul, he dropped the lamp and flung his arms
around his son, embracing him and kissing his cheek.
At the entrance to the living-apartments the family
crowded about him. His mother, Deborah, now reached
up to put her arms about him, and then she laughed and
cried and fondly stroked his young beard. David, a
slender lad, tall for his age, waited in some hesitation,
then greeted Saul. He paused only a moment and ran
to tell his chum, Abiathar, the son of Eleazar, that Saul,
his brother, had returned. A shy little girl whom Saul
could not recognize waited to be told that this was the
elder brother whom she could not remember.

"You should see him!" David was saying to Abiathar,
his friend. "He has such a fine beard. I don't believe
he will ever play ball with us any more."

"I had a dream about him," said Tabitha, who had
been listening to David. "I awakened laughing at the
funny beard he had."

"The oddest thing is that girls always dream about
things they want," said Abiathar, "or they tell them as
dreams."

"You are a barking puppy," Tabitha blushed, "and
I'll have father teach you a lesson." Turning to David,
she asked, "Did he come up directly from Jerusalem?"

"I didn't wait to find out," David replied, "but he
is so sunburned and dusty that he might have come
back by way of Egypt."

"But Egypt is to the south.   He would have had to travel over the world to come home that way," said Tabitha.

"He looks as if he had," said David.   "Come over and see him for yourself."

"Not so," said Tabitha, "until he has rested, and then should he want us to come, he will let us know."

"Now you can go to sleep," said Abiathar, teasingly, "and perhaps you can dream that he came here right away."

Tabitha gave Abiathar a stinging slap for reply.

Saul was induced by his gentle mother to remove his dusty clothes, bathe, and eat.   Then he was willing to talk far into the night with her, but, as if he were the lad who only yesterday had left Tarsus, she compelled him to go to sleep, with the admonition that in the morning and in the days to come she would have him tell over and over his life in Jerusalem.

Conversation was an art in those days.   A person told his tale to inform and entertain his hearers.   The thread of the story was not broken with harsh comments. Every traveler was an observer on his own initiative. Those who stayed at home had news equally important to the one who returned.   Conversation was not a series of trivial hop-skipping of superficial comments, inverted, subverted, and diverting expressions.   It was an interchange of facts, impressions, and well-grounded opinions.

Four years of absence gave Saul much anxiety to accommodate himself as a unit in the smooth-running home life.   His next day was devoted to his mother. She not only had an interest in what he had done but all the little details of Martha's home life were as entrancing to her as if she were a child listening to fairy stories.

Above all, she made Saul repeat all the little incidents in the life of Ahiram, Martha's youngest son. The mother gloried in praising Adonijah, whom Miriam had married; she told of the home and the fine business which Adonijah had in Salamis, and that some day they would go over to Cyprus and visit them in their home.

In the evening the whole family gathered in the living-room, resting on the soft cushions, and spent a long time gathering up the missing links of the years. In a lull in the conversation, Saul inquired if Eleazar and his family would come in during the evening.

"They would not intrude on our first night with you, my son," said Ben Hanan, with a meaning look at his wife. "Neither will Ben Arza come, for he well understands that your first night is sacred to our family conferences. They know and observe the right of a family to its own life."

"Perhaps my anxiety to see everyone as soon as possible is too great," said Saul. "I do not want you to feel that I am at all weary of dear little mother." He laid his head in her lap.

Deborah smoothed his hair as caressingly as if he were the small boy of years long ago. The talk ranged from the details of his school life and service in the Sanhedrin to the sights of Damascus and in the vicinity of Antioch. Ben Hanan required Saul to repeat his experience in Damascus and was anxious to know that Saul had taken every precaution in sending his report to Gamaliel. The hour was late.

"I have thought matters over," said Ben Hanan, in a new tone which aroused interest. "I find that the business is growing. It is the business of this family, now that grandfather is gone. He enjoined me to make such preparations as I now propose; in fact, have made, in part. Saul will have to give much of his time to our people, for they need him, and they expect it of him because of his preparation. While he cannot give all his time to the business, what time he can give will relieve me. David, do you want to grow into the business?"

"I certainly do," said David.

"Then, Saul, the time may come when you may need rooms for your own use." Ben Hanan's voice was softer than it had been. "When you do, remember that I have purchased a parcel of land adjoining our home, and have set aside a fund for you to construct your building, of course to be charged against your final interests in the business. Your first duty is to teach as much as possible. Ben Arza wants your help. If the terms suit you, then you will know how to order your affairs, unless it be that your experience in Damascus lures you back to Jerusalem."

"My life lies here in Tarsus, and my debt to you cannot be paid except in the service that will please you." Saul spoke as if it were a vow.

"I am glad to hear you say so," said Ben Hanan, "for in my talk with Ben Arza today he told me that he would like, if we were willing, to read your credentials to the congregation next Sabbath, and to secure the consent of the council of the synagogue to confirm you as rabbi. I thought it good."

"That is so quickly done, I fear it may be offensive to some of our people," said Saul.

"Our people have patiently waited four years for this event," said Ben Hanan.

Saul sprang up and disappeared for a brief space of time. When he came back he was carrying a package in his girdle. He helped his mother to rise. He unloosed the package and the rich folds of a silk veil, mounted on a headdress, rippled down almost to the floor.

"I did not intend to bring this out until the beginning of the Sabbath," Saul said, as he put the veil on his mother's head, "but I want little mother to know that she has as handsome a veil as anyone, when Sabbath comes."

The joy of the mother amply repaid Saul, and the admiration of the rest of the family was so great that she scolded them for trying to make her vain.

They did not neglect the custom of their times, even at that late hour. There was a slight pause, and Ben Hanan asked Saul to lead in the prayer of the evening. The influence of the custom was to make the family loyal to one another, to give them a sense of consecration and a feeling that they were safeguarded in the struggles and uncertainties of life. In these devotions there was no feeling of compulsion, no humiliation; but in pride and joy, from the eldest to the youngest, there was a feeling that the prayer was a privilege. At least, its results could be seen in the joy of the home life, and in the confidence with which every member went to his tasks, as well as the patience with which he met adversity.

Saul recited one of the prayers selected for the evening service:

"O Lord, Our God! Cause us to lie down in peace, and raise us up again to life! O, Our King! Spread over us the tabernacle of Thy peace; strengthen us before Thee in Thy good counsel, and deliver us for Thy name's sake. Be Thou for protection round about us; keep far from us the enemy, the pestilence, the sword, famine and affliction. Keep Satan from before and from behind us, and hide us in the shadow of Thy wings, for Thou art a God who helpest and deliverest us; and Thou, O God, art a gracious and merciful King. Keep Thou our going out and our coming in, for life and for peace, from henceforth and forever!"

"Eleazar and his family will be over tomorrow evening with us," softly spoke Deborah to Saul as they parted for the night.

CHAPTER XV

WOOING TABITHA

In the early morning Saul went into the workroom, where David sat at the loom. A stranger was sewing the tent-cloth.

"This is a heavy task," said David, "but father says you learned it and that I must."

"I am glad that I was kept at it," said Saul, as he took a seat by the side of David and showed him how to weave the tent-cloth water tight.

"You have not forgotten how to do it, in all these years," David said in admiration.

"I kept in practice while living with Ben Gerber," said Saul. "Who gives you your lessons in the Law?"

"Mother teaches me some, and after the morning hour I go to school to Ben Arza. It is well they did not try to make a rabbi out of me, for I do not take to so much learning. You are to give me lessons, and that will be hard on both of us."

Saul smiled and went over to the place on the dais where the grandfather used to sit. He saw that the same cushions were there, dusted and well-kept. The workman told him that no one was permitted to sit there. Saul, gently lifting the largest cushion, saw the slab his grandfather had raised. He lifted it. In the cavity lay the roll he had seen before. Reverently he put things back in place and went to the front booth, where his father was busy with customers. Saul lingered until there was no one in the booth save his father.

"I thought I could spend some time learning your ways of business," said Saul.

"It would be better for you to visit Ben Arza and Nestor and your old athletic director. You ought to get yourself thoroughly back into Tarsus, my son, before you take up a business that has run for so many years in a certain way that our customers would leave us, if there were any change. I want you to visit until after the Sabbath, for a man cannot pick himself up from Jerusalem and in a day replace himself in Tarsus after years of absence."

Saul went to the synagogue and found that the years were telling on Ben Arza, but the joy of the old rabbi at meeting with Saul was so great that he kept repeating:

"So your first visit out of the house was to see me?"

Saul noticed that the rabbi tactfully refrained from discussing any of the manifold questions which he remembered he had loved to discuss with Azel, but told him about the members of his congregation.

"You will want to know what my understanding of the Law is," said Saul.

"Have you consented to the plan your father requested?"

"Yes, but still you always examined me carefully."

"That was before you went to Gamaliel. Now it is enough to know that Gamaliel has commended you. I think it would be wise for you to meet your old friend, Nestor. I think much of him and he asks about you."

This was a new note in Ben Arza's life. He had made friends with a Gentile. With curiosity as to the attitude of Nestor, Saul went to the old hall, where he had often listened to the lectures, and found Nestor before a class. Saul paused and looked about the room, and was struck with the beauty of the surroundings. While he had seen more grandeur in buildings, the riot of statuary in Antioch, yet the quiet beauty of the hall called back the descriptions by Nestor of the Parthenon, and the lesson that he sought to give of simplicity in expression. Nestor stopped his lecture and made his way to Saul.

"I would not have known you," said Nestor, "unless my friend Ben Arza had told me that you had returned. Come, let me present you to my class."

"I am surprised that you and Ben Arza are such friends."

"Not more than we are," said Nestor, smiling. "We happened to meet in my inquiries about you; and we found that each of us has an honest desire to know God, he coming from Sinai and I from Olympus."

Nestor led Saul before the class and introduced him as a young Hebrew who had once been in the school, and since had been a student under the greatest Hebrew teacher, Gamaliel. Saul responded in general terms, telling of his pleasure and advantage in having been under Nestor; of the great lessons he had learned from him of how to be a gentleman; he said the greatest lesson learned under him was to be open-minded and tolerant.

From the hall Saul went to the gymnasium to meet the director, who had no warning of his visit.

"Jew that you are," said the director, "yet I know that you have been under me. Do not tell me your name. That beard puzzles me. You were a lad—lay off that long outer coat. Now I know you. Yes, there is that tiny scar on your forehead. Saul—'aye, Grotius has come in.' And you have grown. Let me feel those muscles. Fine, but not in training. You should keep up some training, for you have wonderful development that should not be allowed to grow flabby."

"I have come back to live in Tarsus, and perhaps I'll come to the gymnasium once in a while."

"Do so freely," said the director. "I will keep you in condition till you have come to your solid manhood."

"Even now I would like to swim in the pool once more."

"I was about to take a plunge myself," said the director. "Join me."

After swimming in the pool Saul felt refreshed and that he was more nearly able to fit in the years of absence as part of his life in Tarsus. He remembered the quay where he used to loiter, and he went down the street which had been decorated by Antony at the reception of Cleopatra. Many of the columns were still standing, but no effort was made to keep the street in repair.

At the wharf were camels and donkeys, men and goods, a small boat, slaves, and the hubbub of merchants bartering, as if he had been absent only a day. To add to the impression of the brief passage of time, a small company of Roman soldiers rode up to the wharf, dusty from travel, and unloaded their small baggage; the soldier in charge of the company directing his men to get aboard the boat.

On his way back from the wharf he called to see his old friend, the Sadducee boy, but he had gone to Ephesus. He soon became accustomed to the veiled women on the streets, for some were veiled in Jerusalem, and he remembered that all honorable women wore veils in Tarsus.

Late in the afternoon he returned home; it had been a wonderful day to him, but he keenly anticipated the visit of Eleazar and family that night. He was more worried about how to address Tabitha, what she would be, what would be her attitude toward him, than he had been about any of his experiences of the day.

His mother had laid out his finest robe, cleaned and white; she had shaped his headdress so that he could wear it; and he knew from her absence that she was busy preparing an extra meal for the evening. His doubts were largely removed as he looked at his finest robe, for certainly Tabitha would be impressed with his appearance, and she would be, like all the others, glad to welcome him back.

The meal was spread, the cushions were arranged for all to recline while they ate. He was so impatient that he feared the guests would not come. In due season his father led the guests in. Saul was greeted warmly by Eleazar and his wife, but Tabitha hung back timidly and softly spoke her welcome, without lifting her veil as her mother had done. The young girl was just budding into womanhood, the marriageable age, according to custom. She had grown nearly as tall as Saul; and, notwithstanding her veil covered the lower part of her face and shoulders, it could be seen that she had a well-rounded form. She moved with grace and had the rare charm of true modesty. Saul was disappointed that he could not see her face, since she would not remove her veil, even though others had done so, in the sanctity of the family circle. Even she contrived to be so placed at the meal that her mother shielded her from the eyes of Saul, when her veil was thrown back while eating. She evaded entering into the table talk, more than to give the shortest and most direct answers to any questions. She avoided any extended replies to Saul's references to their life before he left the city.

Saul had tried desperately to engage Tabitha in conversation after all had dined. Finally, taking from his girdle the napkin which she had given him when he left, he unfolded it, saying to her:

"See, I have always had a sample of your needle-work with me."

"It was not well done," she replied, very evenly, "for it was my earliest work."

"I wish I might see your last work," said Saul eagerly.

"It is hardly proper that an unmarried girl should display her handiwork," she said with averted eyes, "after she becomes a woman, for then she regards it differently. It is more sacred than when she was a child."

In that simple statement, more by the tone than by the words, it was revealed to Saul that Tabitha was now a woman, and he knew that she had to be won as a woman. Her modesty was a labyrinthine fence about her, which could not be rudely broken down; but it was plain that she wished to be approached along the wind-ing way, without disclosing too quickly the entrance to the path that led to her guarded self. All his sustaining vanity left him. Resentfully he thought that he would pursue the subject no farther; but there surged back on him the sweet tenderness of her; the dignity and caution with which she had urged her rights; the delicacy with which she had let him understand that a maiden counted it a thing of value to be won; and perhaps, after all, she would hesitate to give him the favorable answer. His pride was hurt. The necklace he had brought from Jerusalem could rest undisturbed.

Thoughts of the first Sabbath after his return home gave him more anxiety than had any of the preceding events in his life. While he expected favorable results, yet he felt unduly agitated. The synagogue was crowded. Even on the side set off by a screen for the women, the space was crowded. The people stood. A platform extended a considerable distance from the back end toward the front across the room. On this platform were the only benches in the synagogue, and on these benches, facing the audience, were seated the members of the local Sanhedrin of Tarsus, including the council of the synagogue.

Near the front of the platform was the reading stand or pulpit on which was placed the roll of the Law, on two rollers; by winding the long belt or strip onto the right-hand roller and off the left-hand roller, the reader could read the Hebrew text—this being a synagogue of strict Pharisees the Greek text was not used. At the back end of the bema, or platform, was a curtain, in imitation of the Temple, concealing from view the reproduction of the ark of the covenant and rolls of the Law and of the Prophets.

Ben Arza announced that Saul would read the lessons for the day, and would not need any interpreter, for usually an interpreter was needed to translate the Hebrew into Aramaic, the spoken language of the Jews. Saul could not resist trying to catch a glimpse of Tabitha through the screen, but their veils added to the screen's concealment of the women. The duties assigned to Saul carried also the pronouncing of the benedictions, the shema, or morning prayer, the benediction at the close of the reading, and the translation. He had gone through with this program many times before, and it was easy enough for him to follow it, almost mechanically.

"Say what is in your mind," said Ben Arza, when Saul had finished. While Saul knew that, according to custom, he was expected to deliver an address, in the nature of an account of his time spent in the Holy City, yet he hoped to escape it, for he thought of himself as a youth in the congregation.

He arose to acknowledge the request from Ben Arza and when he turned to the audience the faces blended into a blurred mass. He even fancied that through the lattice he could see a pair of big brown eyes smiling at him over a veil. His hands were cold, his lips were dry, and he felt the hot blood rush to his face. He stepped forward and took the chair provided for the one who gave the address, although the reader stood when reading. He began very humbly, hesitatingly referring to his early days in Tarsus, and how it had been on his mind all the time to return and take up his life among his own people.

The spell was broken and, his nervous temperament now controlled, he was absorbed in the telling of his story, so that his words shot forth as if urged by a torrent of feeling.

In his energy he forgot the time and place and arose, after the manner in the Greek school, pouring out his soul in the great thought that the time was now at hand for every effort to bring men to observance of the law and to make the sacrifices of repentance. Then it came to him that he was standing; but, without any embarrassment, he continued his talk while taking his seat. He had spread the spell of his personality over the people, and they murmured in approval when he had finished.

At the close of Saul's talk, Ben Arza came forward and announced that the president of the council had a word to say.

"My word is short, and very properly Ben Arza might have said it himself," said the president. "It is this: We have asked Ben Arza to instal Saul as an associate rabbi of this synagogue, with the hearty approval of Ben Arza. If anyone has aught to say against it, let him speak."

"Since no one speaks, we will take it that the congregation approves," the president continued, after a pause for an objection. "Saul, kneel, and Ben Arza will pronounce the benediction."

The simple ceremony was soon performed, for it was merely a confirmation by the members of the synagogue of the more elaborate examinations and ceremony through which Saul had passed in Jerusalem.

The following week Saul plunged into the details of business. He found that his father had been so scrupulous in keeping accounts that he knew to whom he had sold goods for many years, the prices and quality; that he had a perfect knowledge of almost the exact time that a customer would return from the distant mountains or from the desert for a duplicate order. He had complete memoranda of sources of supplies and prices, and of those who exchanged supplies for the manufactured goods. Thus began Saul's schooling in business affairs. On the day of the middle of the week Ben Hanan told

Saul to prepare himself early in the evening to sup with Eleazar.

"Do you think, father," said Saul with the utmost frankness, "that I may pursue Tabitha with justice to her and to myself?"

"A maiden must be won," said the father, "before the business of talking about settlements is taken up. Your own heart must guide you; and you will scarcely think her worthy in after-years, if you have not the desire so strong to make her your wife that you can win her to your way of thinking."

In Eleazar's house that evening, Tabitha was busy serving the meal. She had tied the long, loose sleeves of her outer dress back of her shoulders, and the tight sleeves of her under garment were rolled up out of the way, disclosing a beautiful, rounded arm. She had laid aside her veil. Her large, luminous, brown eyes glowed above her olive-hued, oval face. The warm blood tinted her skin and made red her lips, of delicate shape. Saul's eyes followed her as if in hunger they were feasting. She was a brighter vision than his fancy had painted. Womanhood was glorified in her. She went about her tasks in a quiet way, apparently oblivious to the burning eyes with which Saul watched her every movement.

Eleazar proposed that all should go up to the house-top to enjoy the cool breezes of the evening after the meal had been finished and the dining mat had been cleaned. Saul lingered to the last, helping his mother up the narrow stairway. At the top he looked back to see if Tabitha had come. His mother said she wished he would go back and get her veil, as she feared that later the night air would be cool, but that he need not hurry.

Tabitha was sitting on a dais with some of her work, as if she intended to make an evening of it by the lamp.

"I thought you would come with us," said Saul, as he took his mother's veil from a small table.

"I could not see to work up there, and, besides, they would want you to tell them again and again about your wonderful Gamaliel," she said, in even tones.

"Do you not like him?" Saul was sitting down beside her while he spoke.

"Well enough," replied Tabitha, "but a woman has many things to think of besides the dividing of the word."

"Let me speak quickly, lest someone interrupt us." Saul's words came with the stress of his feeling. "You know, Tabitha, I carried the napkin all these years, because I thought of you. A little thing, but I come back to win the hand that made it!"

"A woman wants something more than honors, laws, and discussions," Tabitha spoke as she stitched precisely.

"That is right, and a man needs something more than a knowledge of all learning and wisdom to fill his life out and make living a joy." Saul's tense voice was the note of love. "All that is for you and, more, I want my life to be for you."

"Until you said in the synagogue that you had come back to live here," her voice was now vibrant, "I did not think you had enough love to hold the life of a woman in your keeping; but when I saw how afraid you were to go on with your talk at the request of Ben Arza, I was ashamed lest my eyes would disclose how my heart warmed to you."

"I did see your eyes through the screen, through your veil; those wonderful eyes of yours, limpid as the depths of the sea, bright as the stars of night." He was singing the song of his passion for her. "Here, see!" He drew from his girdle the necklace. "I loved you when away and brought this to seal our betrothal."

She bowed her beautiful head of shining black hair toward him to receive it about her neck. Trembling with emotion, he slipped it over her head. She dropped her work and leaned over on his shoulder. A new world had been created for them, or, rather, the old world had been revealed to their exalted vision as a place of wondrous beauty. Thoughts flashed from soul to soul.

"Let us go up to the roof," she said shyly. "I do not think it is too dark for them to see your present, and to hear what we have to tell them."

CHAPTER XVI

A LOVER-HUSBAND

The questions of marriage settlements were adjusted by the parents of Saul and Tabitha, so that she had a fund that would, if need arose, be hers, separate from the claims of her husband; but the management of it was given to Saul, as was the custom. The banns were announced in the synagogue many days before the time of the wedding. Every step in a marriage was designed to make the union solemnly binding. While divorce, as a mere procedure, was easy and involved little detail, yet back of the marriage was such strong sentiment of the people upholding it that rarely did anyone resort to divorce, having the fear of public opinion before him. By the publicity given to the banns there was an assurance that no scandal, no concealment, no secret living would be allowed to interfere with a proper union.

The marriage ceremony of Saul and Tabitha followed in due course. It involved a procession to the synagogue under the canopy borne by four attendants, the trumpets preceding, the bearer of palm and myrtle branches leading the way, and attendants scattering wheat and sometimes small coins, in token of plenty. Standing before the altar and under the canopy, the marriage contract was read to the bride and groom; the scarf was spread over their shoulders; the cup of wine was tasted and the cup was thrown on the floor and broken, in memory of the vow that their children should be taught to labor for the return of the Hebrew people from their captivity; the ring was blessed and placed on the bride's right forefinger by the groom, with a solemn declaration that it was a symbol of their union.

The joyous procession re-formed and conducted the couple to the groom's home; the bride let down her hair and loosed her veil. Then followed a week of festivities, participated in by the friends and relatives, though the bridal couple celebrated their marriage for thirty days. In the intimacy of home life, marriage was sacred, and the coming of children was hailed as a special favor of God. With no false modesty the family discussed the intimate affairs of life as matters of solemn interest.

Saul built his house as his father had provided; took up his work as a teacher, and strictly followed the strongest injunction laid upon a rabbi—to visit the sick, to care for the fatherless, and to bury the dead. He gave a few hours every day to the business and some special attention to the education of David. His classes were eagerly sought by the youth, so that he had to limit his services to those old enough to understand the higher teaching for which he was fitted.

The devotion he showed his wife was such as to attract the attention of even those who taught the sacredness of the family. It was not a duty that called him to his home, but the great love he bore Tabitha, which grew into worship of her in the passing days. So busy was he with his activities as rabbi and a business man that it was a wonder he had any time for his home; but resolutely he held his allotted time for his wife. She even chided him that he was spoiling her with his many little acts to relieve the tedium of her duties.

"Should a rabbi who is needed as a great teacher give his time to run his wife's errands?" she asked.

"Should my love for you, that knows no bounds, be denied expression for the sake of those who will care little for the sacrifice?" and this question closed all argument from Tabitha.

Nestor invited Saul to lecture before his school on the source of the Hebrew idea of Jehovah. Ben Arza added his commendation of the opportunity, saying that it was a rare thing that a Jew should be called to speak in the hall of a Greek school. To prepare himself for this task required a review of the Greek philosophers, for Saul determined that he would present the subject in such light as would make the understanding of Jehovah easy for the Greek mind. Tabitha firmly insisted that he should give up the doing of small tasks for her until he had completed his preparations.

Saul was surprised at the number of leading men present on the day he addressed the students under Nestor. Nestor made clear that in presenting Saul to make this address he was going outside of the usual customs, but that it could do no harm to hear from one who had been a student in this school concerning things which had a powerful influence in all parts of the world.

When Saul arose to respond he felt imbued with the spirit of the philosophers and prophets. He was not conscious of self, but thrilled with the thought that here he might plant the seed which would yield a bountiful harvest in the years to come. He knew that he was to speak to Greeks and, with a subtlety that seemed to come unsummoned, he spoke in the rounded and finished tones of a Greek. He led them in a review of their own philosophers who had sought the one great and Supreme Spirit back of the mysteries of creation; he pointed out how selfish teachers had perverted the view of the great men of Greece; he passed with quick but biting sarcasm the idle efforts of the Gnostics to catch the unwary by establishing the doctrine of a multitude of spirits intervening between man and the great First Cause.

Then, with a trick of abruptness he had shown in Damascus and which he developed later in life, he asked:

"What do you seek? God over all? If so, why do you limit him with your reason? Your spirits will tell you when you have known God, if it so be that you earnestly seek him. In your heart being convinced that there is a God, from whom proceeds life and every good thing, would you shut your eyes to further visions of his power and how to reach him?

"The Hebrew mind accepts the premise that there is a God who rules, from whom life proceeds," he declared. "When the fathers of the Hebrew people accepted this premise as universal knowledge, with unrestrained faith, they sought to bring their spirits into harmony with God by searching out every ultimate good, and found that it was embodied in the God of our people and of any people who have the faith to accept him. Hence, faith is the foundation of the understanding that the Hebrew people have of the Lord our God. If he were the creation of any mortal mind, then it would be found that there were. faults in his attributes. He is spirit; personified in speaking of him, to make him comprehensible to man. In all the ages it is found, by reasonable and fair investigators, that the Lord God is unmoved from the seat of righteousness.   He can do no wrong."

The audience listened to the full discourse of Saul with candor and his reputation grew in Tarsus so that on any Sabbath when he was to speak in the synagogue there were many Greeks in attendance.

Ben Hanan was overjoyed at the progress Saul was making, and tried to keep him from giving too much time to the business; but Saul urged that age was coming on his father and that soon there would be additional demands upon his own earnings in his own family. Ben Hanan was pleased and agreed that it was right that Saul should try to increase the profits of the business.

Among the dealers who came to the shop of Ben Hanan was a tall, robust man from Cyprus, by the name of Barnabas.   He had heard Saul in the synagogue and urged him to come to Salamis.

"I would like to come," said Saul in answer to the urging of Barnabas, "to visit my sister, Miriam, and meet her husband, Adonijah; but I cannot leave home until my child is born."

"If soon, it would be well to wait," said Barnabas.

"Not that I could not make the journey before that event," said Saul, "but I would not leave my wife for a day until the babe rests in her arms."

Tabitha tried to argue against Saul excusing himself from the synagogue and earnestly endeavored to convince him that he should go about his regular duties. Even his mother urged him that every care would be given Tabitha.

"It matters not what care you give her," Saul said with finality. "She is my wife and I am only giving her the attention that is her due."

When Saul's first-born son arrived there was not only great rejoicing in the families of Ben Hanan and Eleazar, but from outside of Jewish circles came presents and good wishes. Then it seemed almost impossible for Saul to leave the side of his wife and their little son, whom they had named Jonathan. They had also given him the Roman name of Nestor.

Saul's intense devotion to Tabitha seemed to grow with every passing day. The floodgates of love had been opened through which the intensity of his nature sought expression.

"Sometimes I fear that our intense love will consume itself or that we will be overtaken by tribulation," said Tabitha.

"No danger that it will consume itself," said Saul, "for it feeds itself; and if misfortune overtake us, then we will have lost none of the joy of life."

After the boy had grown to sturdy babyhood, Saul was persuaded by Ben Arza and Tabitha to accept an invitation to Salamis for a short stay, giving a series of lessons and lectures to the Jews and to many Greeks attracted by his reputation.

"My heart warmed to you," said Barnabas, after Saul had finished in Salamis, "when I heard you in Tarsus, and I was resolved then to have you come to us in Salamis. I am glad that you came."

"I shall always remember your kind treatment," said Saul, "and I hope some day to come again, but now I must hasten home."

Nestor called on his friend Ben Arza to learn what were the qualifications for a member of the Greater Sanhedrin. "Do you think of listing your name for a membership?" asked Ben Arza with a laugh.

"Not so," said Nestor, "lest I fail to give even your ten words rightly. It seemed to me that Cilicia should be entitled to a member; and if I gather rightly your law, your associate Saul is now qualified. Suppose that you suggest it to your proper dignitaries; and, in my answer to a letter from Gamaliel asking for my views on the influence of Philo's writings, I will mention that this Saul seems eminently qualified to represent this section of the country in your greater senate."

"That will I gladly do," said Ben Arza warmly. "Saul needs something to take him away from Tarsus once in a while. He is so desperately in love with his wife that he may stick right here and hide his ability needed to put life in the Sanhedrin."

So it came to pass that when Saul's son was a year old, there came a letter from Gamaliel, telling Saul that at the next Passover the Greater Sanhedrin would meet and that, since he had been selected as the new member from Cilicia, he must be present, by all means. Ben Hanan took the letter and read it over carefully two or three times. Then he went out and closed the booth, though it was several hours before the time of closing. He sent for Ben Arza, Eleazar, for the president of the local Sanhedrin, for prominent members of the council of the synagogue. He hailed a baker, a butcher, a wine merchant, and commanded a greater feast than had ever been served in his house.

When he came back Tabitha was in the midst of the most tearful expostulation with Saul.

"Would you allow our selfish love to spoil the most splendid opportunity of your life?" she was saying.

Ben Hanan heard the question and gathered the reason for it. Before he could speak, Ben Arza hurried in and cried, breathlessly:

"What mean you by this, Ben Hanan?"

"I mean that we should rejoice, for the Lord has done great things for us."

"But have you asked Nestor to this feast?" Ben Arza asked, accusingly.

"It is among our own people," said Ben Hanan.

"What greater friend has Saul than Nestor, who threw the Roman influence in the scales to gain this very thing for Saul?" said Ben Arza with passion.

"I will hasten to ask Nestor myself to the feast. If he will come, we will be glad." Suiting his action to the word, Ben Hanan left at once.

Saul was so amazed that he simply looked at all inquiringly, without saying a word. Tabitha was overjoyed. Deborah was holding the baby and tears of joy were falling down her face. Rabbi Ben Arza began talking with David about the conditions of trade. Saul felt that he was not really a part of the strange tableau, he was on the outside, looking in on himself. Argument had ceased.

Tabitha induced Saul to change his clothes while she assisted Deborah in preparing for the guests. It was a time for him to think, and while not abating his intense love for his wife and home life, he fully surrendered to the idea that it was his duty to accept the wider field of service and to forego his personal feelings.

Nestor made himself at ease among the other guests assembled for the feast, with the good-natured adaptation of the polite Greek gentleman. Saul, on entering the room, went directly to Ben Hanan; and, folding his arms across his breast, he knelt to his father as he had done in childhood. Placing his hand on Saul's head Ben Hanan recited a blessing, so low that none but Saul heard it. Then Saul accepted the congratulations of the guests and a benediction by Ben Arza. Deborah came into the room and Saul hurried to her and knelt for her hand to be placed upon his head.

"Go to Tabitha," said Deborah, after placing her hand on his head, "for her blessing should be given to you alone."

"Now I know what you mean," said Nestor to Ben Arza, as Saul was leaving the room, "when you tell me that the Hebrews have spiritualized the every-day things of life."

The feast of rejoicing extended far into the night.

CHAPTER XVII

THE PASSING YEARS

Saul journeyed to Jerusalem at the next Passover, and took his place among the members of the Greater Sanhedrin, now acting in his own right and not as a substitute for an absent member. The meeting with his teacher was a revelation to him of the wide knowledge Gamaliel had of affairs throughout the Roman Empire, and of the clearness of his vision as to the relations of Jews to the government.

"Our people must be brought to the highest spiritual state possible," said Gamaliel, "before they can stand for any demand of rights from Rome which the emperor does not willingly grant. Our exclusiveness arouses suspicion in every land; our persistence excites animosity; our intolerance of other religions provokes strong prejudices. We must open the way as much as possible for others to become partakers of our faith. We must conciliate the nations."

Age was beginning to show upon Gamaliel in his rapidly whitening hair, and his opinions seemed to grow more tolerant. The infinite details to which the government of the Temple had been extended were more distinctly impressed upon Saul's mind than in his former sojourn. He lodged with his sister, Martha, and her husband, Ben Gerber, and he found his nephew rapidly growing, a sturdy little fellow. This opportunity to observe the life of another family brought him to a high appreciation of the duties prescribed in the home life

of his people. He had lived under such complete observance of the regulations for the family that he had not before
thought of the importance of the family life in the scheme
of his religion; nor had he before paused to trace the far-
reaching influence of home life upon the Jewish people.

On his return to Tarsus from his first sitting as a
member of the Sanhedrin, Saul plunged into the busy
life laid out for him with even increased energy. The
years sped along rapidly. David had married; another
child had come to Saul's home. His fame as a speaker
had grown, so that at last he could no longer resist
another invitation to go to Salamis. He visited cities
along the coast, upon their urgent request. The greatest
difficulty for him to overcome was his absence from his
wife and family; even Ben Arza chided him with being
more concerned with courting Tabitha than with the
reality of a home.

Then there were other visits to Jerusalem to settle
the many questions of approval of laws brought down by
tradition so that they would have the authority of the
Sanhedrin; as well, there were questions relating to
government. Always some devout men were urging
such steps as would challenge the rule of Rome, and
irresponsible agitators stirred the people with false
hopes—in some instances pretending they were the men
of whom the prophets had spoken as the deliverers of the
children of Israel. These pretenders had to be dealt
with by the Sanhedrin to make it plain to Rome that
the rights given the Jews would not be used in rebellion
against the Empire.

Ben Hanan was growing old, not beyond usefulness,
but he was not so active in the conduct of the business

as in former years. David had rapidly developed a genius for the handling of the business, but he insisted on having the advice and help of his elder brother.

Nine years had slipped away in the busy life of Saul. Nestor had been laid away in a tomb on one of the hills overlooking his beloved school. Two other children had come to Saul and Tabitha; and all, except the first-born, had been taken away by a fatal epidemic.

The trade caravans were increasing in numbers, coming down through the Cilician gates from the lands on the hither side of the desert, adding to the trade of Tarsus and the business of the house of Ben Hanan.

Saul had not attended the last two principal meetings of the Sanhedrin because he was in mourning for his children and he would not leave Tabitha to bear her grief alone.

PART IV

The Valley of Shadows

CHAPTER XVIII

THE MOURNER

The letters from Gamaliel had grown so urgent that Saul had promised to be present at the next convocation of the Greater Sanhedrin. At the time he should start Tabitha was taken ill with a strange malady. By day and by night Saul waited on her, but the most attentive care available was not enough to save her life. He would not go to the Sanhedrin after her death. He spent the allotted days in mourning and then spent many other days in private mourning. The call of duty fell on his deaf ears. Silently, solemnly, he went about the lighter tasks of the shop, without referring to his grief. His manner was such that neither his father, nor his mother, nor Ben Arza dared speak to him about Tabitha. He would sit long hours by the side of his sleeping son, gazing on his face, the image of Tabitha. He would spend the hours of the morning sewing tent-cloth without speaking a word. His eyes were dry, strained, and deep-set from the intensity of his emotion.

To the request for his help in the synagogue he simply replied to Ben Arza, "Not yet."

Then Ben Arza dispatched a long letter to Gamaliel, telling him all that had happened to Saul and his fear that Saul would lose his mind in his great grief; he urged that Gamaliel should make some special plea to persuade Saul to visit Jerusalem, that haply new surroundings would give him relief from his sorrow.

In the course of time, a long letter from Gamaliel to Saul set forth the many distressful things menacing the welfare of the faith, and that it would be necessary to have some of the most reliable members of the Sanhedrin in a long session to settle important questions, many of which were doctrinal. By the same means Martha had sent him a letter, begging him to make their house his home for a long visit.

In the family conference it was decided that Saul should go. David would take care of the business and Deborah would be pleased to care for Saul's little son, Jonathan.

Saul, now thirty years old, had the appearance of middle age. His grief had robbed him of the kindly smile that had been characteristic of him. His eyes were bright, but burned with suppressed emotion. In this changed demeanor he set off for the journey, now grown familiar to him.

In Jerusalem he made his home with his sister. After three weeks a letter came from his father, telling him that, within a week after he left, Jonathan had sickened and passed away in two days.

For many days Saul sat in the upper room of his sister's house, where years before he had brooded a whole day on his first visit to the city, imagining troubles that might come to him. Now he was in the depths of grief. The son whose face recalled the beloved mother had been taken from him. His burdens were many. He turned to the lamentations of the fathers; he repeated the psalms and prayers of resignation. The cold comfort of all commentaries was that he was suffering for some sin that he had done, and yet he knew that he had lived in good conscience. The law taught that he must expiate the sin, he must repent.

He had sounded the depths of grief. The only relief for him was to become absorbed in zealous service. After spending the allotted days in mourning for his son, he grimly resolved to do all in his power to lose himself in the activities of life. With a vow to summon all his strength and give it to the multitude of affairs coming before the Sanhedrin, he had his hair shorn and made his sacrifices in the Temple.

He wrote a letter to his father, saying:

Saul, the son, to Ben Hanan and Deborah, wise, patient and forbearing father and mother.

The blessings of Israel be on you, may joy be your portion and may I, a selfish, grieving son, cast no shadow on you!

It was well that I came here; for in the courts of the holy Temple my mind has cleared and strength has been given me to endure all affliction. I was reading what the rabbis have written on the loss of a wife. It is:

"If death hath snatched from thee the wife of youth,
　It is as if the sacred city were,
　And e'en the Temple, in thy pilgrim days,
　Defiled, laid low, and leveled with the dust.
　The man who harshly sends from him
　His first-wooed wife, the loving wife of youth,
　For him the very altar of the Lord
　Sheds forth its tears of bitter agony."

I am thankful that every thought of mine was given to Tabitha; that the grief has been so great: for it betokens that in no hour of weakness will I ever forget the love she gave me. And Jonathan was her very image. Again I thank you that you have given me the faith to know that our spirits are immortal. I find strange things here; devout men without faith; leaders without courage; and our religion subject to the whim of politics.

I do not know when I shall return, but tell David to conduct the business as if I had no interest in it, for now it does not matter to me. I have my hands with which to live. In love I cherish you and little sister, David and his wife. Martha and Ben Gerber send their love to you. Commend me to Ben Arza. I am resolved to become busy in affairs and lay aside, if possible, this sorrowful countenance and be worthy as your son.

SAUL

CHAPTER XIX

THE NEW WAY

Saul found an air of uncertainty in the Sanhedrin; a timidity he had never known in the years before now delayed action upon even matters of mere interpretation. Much discussion was had about the course to be pursued with the Jews who were giving their time to the new teaching. Saul inquired what was in this new teaching.

"It is the doctrine that would destroy our work," said Caiaphas, who was presiding at the time, "and would lead men away from support of the Temple, as their leader taught."

"Who was this leader?" asked Saul.

"He was a deluded man from Galilee who created a great furor with his attacks upon the law and the worship in the Temple. He was crucified during the Passover, as you remember," replied Caiaphas.

"I have not been here for three years," said Saul, "and I knew nothing of it, more than by rumors which did not agree."

"It was at the Passover before last," said Caiaphas, "that the people demanded his execution. For some time after it his followers were afraid to make themselves known, but recently they are becoming bolder and are active in stirring up the people with the idea that he was a prophet and a great leader. They have won over many to their way of thinking, which does not help in the devotions of the Temple."

"Why do you not bring them here for discipline?" Saul urged.

"We hesitate to do so," answered Caiaphas. "Besides, we had two here before us not long since, and had to let them go. It is hard to get proof against them and the people may take sides with them. And if we stir up too much trouble at this time, the Roman government may change its policy toward us."

"Have you called in Gamaliel on this question?" Saul asked.

"Yes," was the reply, "and we find that he relies more on the justice of our cause than on the use of force. He it was who led us to release the others."

"Have you not done anything? Do you intend to let this schism grow to the destruction of true worship?" Saul cried out in protest against the indifference with which he thought they were treating the question.

"We had, as I said, two fisherman of Galilee before us and questioned them," said Caiaphas. "They were so zealous and extravagant that it seemed an act of kindness to let them go, after we had warned them that they must not any longer teach in the name of their prophet. They had a poor fellow with them who claimed a miracle of healing had been performed upon him, and the people were shouting praises of the healing. We did not dare to offend the people."

"I come from afar to meet with you," said Saul, "and to help, if possible; but I object to being a party to compromises with error. If you are convinced that these men are subverting the law, leading our people away from the Temple, then we must act promptly and courageously crush out the false teaching."

"You have not gone through what we have," said Caiaphas, "else you would hesitate, lest you bring yourself in danger of these howling fanatics."

"I have been through much," asserted Saul, vehemently, "but now I am here to act and to throw myself into this work."

"Good, good!" shouted many members. "Hail, Saul, hail!"

Saul sprang from the long, black night of his grief into the fierce, burning day of action. The energy that had been suppressed demanded immediate tasks, greater than other men dared to attack. His brain whirled onward and upward, like an eagle in its flight; and, like the eagle's piercing eye, searching out the valleys and mountains far below, his vision swept the depths and heights of experience and prophecy for enemies.

The times needed a voice to awaken men, teachers, and priests; he could almost hear the call of his fathers for sacrifice of self, for one who dared to obey the laws, to keep sacred the worship of Jehovah. The love and honor he had for his beloved teacher should not deter him, and he hastened forth from the Sanhedrin to confer with Gamaliel.

After Saul left the Sanhedrin there was much informal and excited talking among the members, and, upon a sly signal from Caiaphas, a few trusted members lingered to speak with him privately.

"Send men," craftily said Caiaphas, "who will bear such witness as you know we must have, and this can readily be done in the freedom of their discussions in the synagogue. Then we will have these men brought before us for trial in such a way as to arouse the consuming zeal of Saul, without laying ourselves open to the charge of instigating the accusations."

Saul went directly to Gamaliel and was received in the tender, fatherly manner of the white-haired prince, which won for him the adoration of the younger men and the esteem of the elder men. The kindly interest of Gamaliel turned Saul from his purpose for a little while.

"We need the fearless energy and the wise restraint you have, my son," said Gamaliel. "In these times, so perilous to our people, I almost shudder to think what may happen."

"Have not restraint and forbearance gone too far with these agitators of new doctrines?" asked Saul.

"Not from my point of view, for the purposes of God cannot be frustrated by idle words which have the saving grace of love," replied Gamaliel.

"They claim, I am told," urged Saul, "that this Galilean was the Messiah, and yet he made no effort to lead our people."

"I am not exactly certain as to what would be the appearance of the Messiah," said Gamaliel, thoughtfully, "whether he will be only a leader of the people, or whether he will come, as some of the prophets seem to think, as the embodiment of Wisdom."

"We would know our ruler, and we do know that Wisdom is a spirit or influence that enters into the hearts of men, not a personal being," contended Saul.

"I almost agree with you," said Gamaliel, "and yet there comes to me the wonder, in my advancing years, if we are not too sure of our understanding of matters. Would it not be so wonderful as to be the mightiest expression of God, if the spirit of Wisdom were manifested to us in all its purity, in the form of man? Still, it seems that we should not be left in doubt."

"That is the thing that arouses me to action," said Saul. "For those who are faithful to the law would not be denied the knowledge, because the promise is to us. And these agitators, against the very Temple itself, denying to the keepers of the law any part in the knowledge of the coming of the Messiah, without evidence attested by the servants of the law, assert that he has come and has been crucified. They lead our people away, they will destroy our laws, they will cause the Temple to be so deserted that it will be used for the profane purposes of some capricious Roman ruler."

"I would agree with you, if I so understood them," said Gamaliel, "and yet I have the faith to believe in the power of God to sift out the true from the false in the storm of passion."

"But I hold that the servants of the Lord must drive the chariots against the approaching enemy," cried Saul. "My youth is spent, I have no other interest than to serve the Lord with all my strength and with all my soul. This desire has brought me up out of the Valley of the Shadow, and I am here in Jerusalem to give that service."

"And may Wisdom dwell in your heart!" said Gamaliel, placing his hand on Saul's head in blessing, as he had often done in the schooldays.

Saul went out from Gamaliel, feeling that his beloved teacher had permitted his tender regard and great sense of fairness to make him too weak to advise in this situation. Walking along the streets, Saul came to the synagogue of the Freedmen, which he had also known as the Cilician synagogue. A crippled beggar was sitting outside the door, but did not extend his hand for alms as was the usual attitude of beggars on the approach of anyone. This interested Saul so much that he paused to look at him.

"Do you want alms?" said Saul to the beggar. "Then hold out your hand."

"I am not asking alms today," replied the beggar. "I am waiting for the man who is speaking in the synagogue to come forth, and if I have faith like the others, he may heal me."

"Think you a man, not a prophet, could make your crooked legs straight?" said Saul.

"Aye, that he has done for others, I have heard," said the beggar.

"Who is this man, what time has he been anointed for the working of wonders?" cried Saul, as if to confound the beggar.

"His name is Stephen, but I know naught of his anointings. We beggars accept help without knowing if it is from great or small," said the beggar, in apology.

Saul entered the synagogue and listened to Stephen as well as he could. The crowd was so dense that he could not get close to the speaker, and there were several men who were constantly interrupting with questions. He could see Stephen standing on the platform, a fine, large man, middle-aged, and who showed in his weathered face that he had spent much of his time in toil and in the drying winds of Palestine. He was patient with every questioner, giving him an earnest look, as if to answer him to his heart's desire. It was near the close of the meeting when Saul came in and he did not hear much of the discussion. He noted that there were many soberly weighing the questions between themselves.

Among the people he saw some men who were known to be agitators in former years against the Roman government.

Next morning, on his way to the Temple for his devotions, Saul observed dimly in the dawn a crowd assembling near the colonnade on the east side of the court of the Gentiles. He went over to see what was the occasion of the people gathering there at that early morning hour. Priests of the Temple were in the crowd and they helped clear the way for some cripples who were trying to get to the farther side.

"Why the gathering?" Saul asked a priest.

"We are waiting for the teachers of the new Way," the priest replied.

"Why do the cripples push forward?" Saul asked.

"Because these teachers often heal the sufferers by a touch or even a look or a prayer," the priest replied.

"But is it not your place to worship yonder, in the Temple?" Saul asked severely.

"Yes," replied the priest, "but here we learn a new lesson that seems to fill a great place in our hearts that has been empty."

"Then you are deserting the faith of your fathers," said Saul.

"Not at all, only replenishing and increasing that faith, for these tidings are a great consolation to anyone who has longed for deliverance from a sense of guilt. We will go into the Temple and attend our duties there, when it comes time for our watch," replied the priest, as he turned to listen to someone who was speaking from the center of the group.

Saul listened, hoping to hear what the new teacher would say, but all he could hear was the wild declamation of a man telling the story of how he had been healed

simply by lying in the street so that the shadow of
Peter, when passing, fell on him. With a sneer of disgust
Saul crossed the broad court and ascended the steps
leading up to the entrance of the Temple.

The morning light was growing brighter; the doors
were being opened; the sunlight rapidly flooded the
spacious court; and the vista through the eastern gate,
through the Women's Court, up the stairway to the
Gate Beautiful, through the massive Gate Beautiful to
the altar of sacrifice, stretched away to the blazing brass
and gold of the Holy Place, rising in its serene whiteness
as if it were an index to a vision of the worlds beyond.

The beauty and grandeur of the scene revived the
reverence with which he had often stood, as now, in
worship of Jehovah. He had removed his sandals and,
glancing toward the eastern colonnade, he saw the stately
figure of Stephen, whom he had seen the day before in
the synagogue, surrounded by men while he proceeded
on his way. Saul thought to replace his sandals and
join the multitude, but he remembered he was on his
way to his devotions and to turn back now would be to
violate his vows.

In the meeting of the Sanhedrin that day he told of
his experience and complained that no effort was made
to gather the evidence against these men who were leading even the priests of the Temple away.

"Not only must we have proof that will satisfy us,"
said Caiaphas in reply to Saul's complaints, "but it
must be so strong that the procurator will not feel that
he should interfere. Once the cleaning-up of this heresy
is begun, we must follow it until the work is well done.
It has grown every time that we have meddled with it
in only half-way measures."

CHAPTER XX

STEPHEN'S DEFENSE

In the passing days Saul often came upon crowds listening to some teacher giving a harangue on the sins of the times; promising to all who suffered release from their woes, if they would accept the good news and become followers of the Way. Many sick and lame stood up as witnesses, declaring they had been restored, but Saul believed they were hirelings or deceived themselves. He saw poor sufferers who had traveled long distances from the country to be healed by the teachers of the Way. He inquired if the healers asked or received any money or gifts for their services, but found there was no evidence that the healing was for gain.

He learned that they were living in groups and had their goods in common, that they rarely went to the Temple service, though they did not say anything against it, claiming they had not time for devotions in the Temple after they told their story and gave necessary help to others. The rapidly growing popularity of the teaching alarmed him. As soon as a man announced his belief and went through some sort of a baptismal ceremony, such as the Essenes observed, he began immediately to talk to others as if he were a teacher. Saul concluded that it was not only a dangerous thing but that the unusual zeal of converts would spread it beyond all control unless immediately checked.

Then came a day when Saul was hurried from his devotions in the Temple to the Sanhedrin, for the very

Stephen he had seen was to be tried. Saul, upon entering the Hall of Hewn Stone, was surprised to find all vacancies in the Sanhedrin had been filled. The seventy members sat on rugs in a semicircle, facing a long dais, on which, facing the members, were seated three rows of the most learned men then in the city, with the high priest, Caiaphas, on a slightly raised seat, as the presiding officer in the center of the group of learned men. At each end of the dais, thus being at each end of the semicircle of members, was a scribe, standing to make the count when any vote was taken.

Two Temple guards entered, leading Stephen, on whom they had put the dark cloak of mourning, as was the custom. They placed him in the center, facing the semicircle of members. Two witnesses came in and were enjoined to tell the truth.

The first said:

"This man ceases not to speak words against this holy place and the law; for we have heard him say that this Jesus of Nazareth shall destroy this place and shall change the customs which Moses delivered unto us."

The second witness said:

"My brother has said as I would say it, word for word."

The witnesses retired without being questioned by Stephen. Indifferent to his surroundings, he stood erect, his massive head thrown back, his eyes rapturously fixed in a vision and his body tense, as if he heard voices of rare sweetness, speaking an absorbing message to him alone.

Caiaphas, fearing that a spell was being cast over the Sanhedrin, spoke out harshly to Stephen, calling his attention to the witnesses:

"Are these things so?"

Stephen turned in dignity, by his bearing showing that he had no fear of the august assembly, and addressed the high priest, at times turning to the members of the Sanhedrin. He began with the history of Abraham, pointing out that the promises were made him while he was yet in Mesopotamia, that he should be led into a land that would be shown him. In simple, clear phrases he followed the journey of Abraham, ascribing to the God of Glory all the things which Abraham did; that he had been led to this land, in which he had no inheritance, not so much as a place to set his foot. But the promise was made that he and his children should have it for their possession.

Then he told the story of Joseph: how his brethren, because of jealousy, had sold him into Egypt; but that he rose in power until in the famine Jacob, his father, came into Egypt; of the suffering which came to the Hebrews in Egypt.

His story was familiar to his hearers; but it had a charm from his lips, holding them with intense interest, notwithstanding their suspicions that he would pervert it. Stephen moved along with the story of Moses, and gave them a shock with his reference to the incident of Moses defending the Hebrew abused by his task-master, even to the slaying of the Egyptian. He paused, deliberately surveying the teachers seated with Caiaphas, sweeping with searching gaze the whole of the Sanhedrin; then he spoke with impressive emphasis:

"He supposed that his brethren understood that God by his hand was giving them deliverance; but they understood it not."

Caiaphas frowned and the members gave hard looks at Stephen; but as if they were in hearty accord with him he continued the story of Moses; his sojourn in the wilderness, and the call that came to him to be the messenger of God to his people in Egypt.

Breaking away from his recitation of the story, he said, with such force that all his hearers felt the shame:

"This Moses whom they refused, saying, Who made thee a ruler and a judge? him hath God sent to be both a ruler and a redeemer, with the hand of the angel that appeared to him in the bush."

At this declaration the teachers began muttering to one another, protesting that this was not the interpretation. Saul was restrained from breaking out in resentment, only because he, being a younger member, was compelled by courtesy to wait for the elders to express themselves. Before anyone could recover himself sufficiently to reply, Stephen had swept on to the wonders performed by Moses, and then, with an intensely dramatic pause, quoted Moses as saying:

"A prophet shall God raise up unto you from your brethren, like unto me."

Caiaphas turned to comment on this to one of the teachers near him, shaking his head in protest. The members of the Sanhedrin were bewildered, but stubbornly refused to admit to themselves that there was any force in the quotation. Stephen followed quickly with a reference to the worship of the golden calf in the wilderness and the captivity that was the penalty. At his reference to the tabernacle in the wilderness and the building of the Temple, Caiaphas licked his dry lips in feline rage, as if now were the time to spring upon him; the admission would be made.

Stephen referred to the tabernacle and the years it had served; that Solomon built the Temple after the plans of David. Then, with a thrust that cut under and through all the elaborate ceremony in and worship of the Temple, he cried:

"Howbeit, the Most High dwelleth not in houses made with hands; as saith the prophet:

> "'The heaven is my throne,
> And the earth the footstool of my feet;
> Did not my hand make all these things?'"

The boldness of this declaration, based on the Scriptures so familiar to them, threw the whole Sanhedrin into such amazement that for a short space of time no one could answer nor voice his anger. Before they could recover from this stroke, Stephen with blazing courage cried out, as if a prophet announcing doom:

"Ye stiffnecked and uncircumcised in heart and ears, ye do always resist the Holy Spirit; as your fathers did, so do ye. Which of the prophets did not your fathers persecute? and they killed them that showed before of the coming of the Righteous One."

Stephen had been speaking to the members with such superior power that they seemed to squat into the floor as he thundered at them. Turning to Caiaphas, he fastened his intense gaze upon him until the high priest let his eyes fall. Then he finished his indictment with the assumption of an authority over his judges before him: "Of whom ye have now become betrayers and murderers; ye who received the law as it was ordained by angels and kept it not."

After a short time of silence from the bold energy of Stephen's attack, the priests and teachers on the dais joined quickly by the members facing them, hissed, growled, and spat at him. Caiaphas let the tumult continue for a little while, until some began calling for the vote.

"Not today!" said Caiaphas, with assumed impartial air. "The law is that we must not vote on a death penalty the same day of the trial, and we are here to follow strictly the law. You are now dismissed to meet at this time tomorrow, to consider arguments and cast your votes. Meanwhile, the guards will keep the accused in charge."

The guards came through the doors of the council-room and led Stephen away; the members and teachers in great excitement rose, spitting at Stephen, who walked out between his guards as if he were a king being escorted to his throne. Saul, in righteous indignation, was shaking his fist at Stephen, when he caught the calm eye of Gamaliel, looking at Stephen as if himself aloof from the pandemonium.

CHAPTER XXI

THE LAW VOTES

Saul left the Temple area by one of the gates leading down through the ramp to the lower street on the south side. He was in deep thought about the trial, and in his reasoning he ascribed the new doctrine to the party known as the Zealots, now stirring up the people to rebel against the priests and leaders, who had failed (as it was charged) to gain anything for the people.

"I am surprised to meet you here at this time," said Barnabas in his big, hearty way, hailing Saul, who was passing without noticing him.

"No more than I am to see you away from your beloved Cyprus," said Saul.

"I have concluded to live here, and have sold all my possessions in Cyprus," Barnabas replied. "You have changed much since last I saw you."

"A great grief came to me. Tabitha passed away and my only living son died since I came here, a few weeks past." Saul spoke as if he were detached from the experience. "And I have just come from the Sanhedrin, where I have listened to the trial of a man by the name of Stephen, in which it was disclosed what a great danger this new doctrine called the Way is to all our sacred institutions."

"Not so bad as that," said Barnabas, "for it seems to me that it brings hope into the lives of men."

"Hope of what?" Saul showed his old fiery spirit. "This man would defy death. In fact, he convicts himself of death by declaring against the ordinances of the Temple, and he smiles confidently while saying it, as if we were impotent. Such zeal carries men beyond reason and makes them forget their religion."

"I would not go so far as to say that," Barnabas replied, "for the glad tidings that we can have a sure forgiveness of sins and the assurance of a resurrection, by example and beyond any question, are enough to make men pause and consider the man's life and claims through whom such great things come."

"Tell me not that you are one of them," said Saul fiercely. "I have determined to know no friend until I have driven these false teachers from the land."

"And you would not listen to a friend who loves you enough to make much sacrifice for your welfare?" Barnabas asked, earnestly.

"No one could persuade me; I would listen to no one; I will not pity nor spare him," said Saul, with increasing fervor.

"But I pity you. Your zeal would deny the Righteous One, even if he were in your presence. Know this, that love has come into the world and it may envelop you. Farewell!"

"I charge you," said Saul, with measured words, "that you abstain from these things; and that if you are led into them, may you escape me, your friend, for I am now pledged to drive out this heresy, regardless of friends or consequences to them or to myself. Now, as friend, farewell!"

Saul went on his way with resolute stride, forbidding in his majesty of righteous conviction. Barnabas stood watching him in pity; then, shaking his head sorrowfully, he went on his way to a meeting of the followers of the Way in the court of the Gentiles. There he was told by a priest of the Temple all that had occurred concerning the certainty of Stephen's fate, which would be followed by persecution to stamp out the teaching of the things that had been said and done by the Nazarene.

Saul went to his sister's house and was so silent during the evening meal that even young Ahiram's questions, which usually aroused Saul to immediate reply, did not bring him into the conversation. He slept, or rather he lay down on the bed to sleep where his grandfather had passed away. The moonlight streamed through the latticed window as had the sunlight when Azel saw his vision of the Temple. The high tension of his nerves gave Saul visions of the Temple laid low, the woe that would come to the people, and then the words of the rabbis came back to him:

If death hath snatched from thee the wife of thy youth,
It is as if the sacred city were,
And e'en the Temple, in thy pilgrim days,
Defiled, laid low, and leveled with the dust.

His grief was more poignant than it had been in the days when his stunned senses failed to recognize fully his loss. In his desperate efforts to take his mind from thought of Tabitha he reviewed the trial of the day, and dark and portentous plans crowded his reasoning. During the long night his mind so painfully and actively concentrated on his loss of Tabitha, and on the possible loss of the Temple, that he could not sleep. Worn and haggard he took his way in the early morning to his favorite place in the Temple to gain some composure of mind in his devotions.

The Sanhedrin had assembled promptly and the members were waiting for the guards to bring Stephen in, when Saul entered. Gamaliel was on the dais; the three rows for teachers were filled. Caiaphas assumed a more judicial air than on the day before, and the members of the Sanhedrin were grimly silent, in sympathy with the attitude of their president. The guards entered with Stephen, who gave no indication of fear or of interest in the assemblage. Saul noted the concentrated gaze of Gamaliel on Stephen, as if he were searching out some secret of his soul.

Stephen was placed in the center of the assembly, first facing Caiaphas; and then, on direction of the high priest, Stephen turned, facing the members of the Sanhedrin. He looked off and over them, as though they were not sitting there on the floor ready to spring for his life when the time would come to vote.

"Has anyone anything to say for the accused?" Caiaphas inquired.

After a long silence Gamaliel rose, as if to leave.

"Have you no word for us?" said Caiaphas to Gamaliel, and aside, to another teacher, he gave a look of cunning self-congratulation.

"I was leaving before you voted, so as not to interfere with your proceedings," said Gamaliel. "Now that you have called attention to me and thereby to my well-known views, I will repeat what I said when you had the two fishermen before you:

"Refrain from these men, and let them alone; for if this counsel or this work be of men, it will be overthrown; but if it is of God, ye will not be able to overthrow them; lest haply ye be found even to be fighting against God."

Apparently changing his mind about leaving, he took his seat.

Saul's lips were moving silently while Gamaliel spoke. Caiaphas called for the vote, which was taken by each one standing until the scribes announced that all had been counted. The first call was for those who voted "not guilty," but none arose. Then, at the call for those who would vote "guilty," Saul, as the youngest member, was required to vote first.

Saul arose, bursting out vehemently in the quotation from the law, while looking Gamaliel unflinchingly in the face:

> "You shall not consent unto him,
> Nor listen to him;
> Neither shall your eye pity him,
> Neither shall you spare,
> Neither shall you conceal him:
> But you shall surely kill him. . . . .
> You shall stone him with stones that he die;
> Because he has tried to draw you
> Away from the Lord your God."

Gamaliel bowed his head while Saul recited and Saul saw diamond drops trickling down on Gamaliel's silvery beard; but, undeterred by Gamaliel's unpretentious display of feeling, Saul stood resolutely as if inspired to lead in the vote that he felt in his soul was righteous. The others rose rapidly until every member was standing.

"The judgment of the whole Sanhedrin is," said Caiaphas, in a dry, solemn voice to Stephen, after the scribes had announced the vote, "that you be stoned to death."

To all appearances, Stephen had not heard the words, for his eyes were fixed on a vision above him.

Extending his outstretched arms toward his vision, he exclaimed:

"Behold, I see the heavens opened, and the Son of Man standing on the right hand of God."

The members of the Sanhedrin instantly became a howling, jeering mob. They plucked at his garments; they spat at him; and they were about to make the place of judgment the shambles of execution. On call from Caiaphas to proceed according to the law, the chief officer of the Temple came in with twelve priests, already selected by lot for the task; and they led Stephen to the place of stoning. Saul, in his zeal, went with them.

They led Stephen outside of the city and, placing him with his back close to the edge of a cliff over the upper Kidron, they took off their outer garments and threw them down in front of Saul, who stood at the side to see that no mercy should be shown.

The priests selected the stones suitable for their purpose from among the many rocks at hand. Stephen stood up and commended his soul to his Lord. They ordered him to kneel, so that he would be an easier object for their marksmanship. As he knelt, he made them more angry by saying in prayerful tones:

"Lord, lay not this sin to their charge."

The twelve strong men flung the stones at the head of the bowed patriarch with such force as instantly to crush out his life. By examination they made sure that he was dead, and left for the city. Looking back from near the entrance to the city, Saul saw men tenderly gathering up and bearing away the body of Stephen and he was almost sure that he saw the large frame of Barnabas among them.

CHAPTER XXII

RUTHLESS ZEAL

Men who had been sent out by the high priest came before the Sanhedrin during the next few days with reports that while the followers of the Way no longer met in the synagogues (save in the smaller ones) they were meeting by appointment in private houses and that some of them were leaving the city.

"Why do you not arrest them and bring them here?" Saul demanded.

"Because we are only guards from the Temple and have not the authority to do so without special direction," said the leader of the guards. "By the time we return and get the authority from the high priest, the men and women escape from the city or go in hiding. We need one in authority over us."

After waiting until others had an opportunity to speak, no one having volunteered, Saul stepped forth.

"Give me the authority to lead the guards," said Saul, "and I will search out these people from their places of hiding. I will take them from their homes and drag them from their synagogues; only I must know that you will not, through fear, revoke my authority."

"It shall be so," said Caiaphas. "Let all speak."

The scribes took the vote of the Sanhedrin and found no dissenting voice. Then Saul was given any number of guards he might demand, from time to time. He started out with only three, but shortly increased the number to more than a score; for he would drag forth those accused, sending them to prison in charge of guards, and hasten with the remaining guards to the next place.

His first two days' work filled the cells that could be used for prisons in the Temple walls. Guards became exhausted from following him in his rapid search. He tore mothers with babes from their houses and would listen to only one plea, renunciation of the Nazarene.

A panic seized the followers of the Way, and those who could leave made their escape out of the city. All through the night silent figures hastened out on the roads, some to the cave country in the west, but principally to the north, so as to be as far as possible from the city at the break of day. They fled to the cities of Samaria and Galilee, spreading the news of the persecution, carried on with frightful and remorseless energy by the man, Saul of Tarsus. Some fled leaving members of their families in prison, others were compelled to leave some members of their families who could not make the flight.

Saul had found a work suited to his dark, brooding mood. The synagogues had been swept clean of the teachers of the Way and he had set guards to seize them if they returned.

He had in a few days changed the whole atmosphere of the city from one of bitter endurance of the sect to an open persecution of any member found. He diligently sought for the men hailed as teachers and apostles; but they were carefully guarded from his spies and guards or had scattered through the country; some were concealed even in the houses of the priests of the Temple.

The more exhausting his labors, the better it suited his mood. He was changed from teacher and adviser to a warrior of his faith. The strain of the blood of Saul, the son of Kish, raced through his veins; he gloried in the wailing pleas for mercy that fell upon his unheeding ears; he felt that the God of his fathers looked down in approval on him, as the one to crush the enemies of the true faith.

There came a time when few could be found to drag forth, either to prison or to humiliating renunciation. Saul felt that his work had been well done.

Then came the news from nearby and distant towns and cities that the fugitives were active, not only in their teachings, but bitter in stirring up hatred against the administration of the Temple. From the cities of Samaria, from Tyre and Sidon it was reported that the fugitives had come among them; and from Tiberias and Caesarea Philippi came the word that the roads leading to Damascus were dusty with caravans of fleeing proselytes, who were telling their story to every wayfarer. At Saul's request, Caiaphas called a meeting of the Sanhedrin to listen to his plans.

"We have driven out the agitators of this new religion," said Saul, in speaking to the Sanhedrin, "until they dare not show their heads in Jerusalem. But now they have fled to other cities, and I hear that they are making for Damascus, apparently with the purpose of establishing in that city a center of their activities. I hear that they are organized in cities on the way, in which they have left leaders. All our work will be for naught, if we stop with what we have done here. We should send someone with authority to overtake them and send them back here as prisoners, so that they cannot lead astray our people in other cities."

"Who will go?" Caiaphas spoke as if someone of the many members present would volunteer.

While no one offered to go, almost every member had a word of strong approval for Saul's plan, and wound up his remarks by saying that it would need a man of ability and zeal, and one so situated that other duties would not compel his speedy return.

"Strange that in all this discussion," said Caiaphas, "no one seems willing to volunteer for the work, nor to mention the one man who is best prepared and best suited for this heroic task."

While making this speech, Caiaphas cast a quick glance at Saul and all the members, following his eyes, gazed fixedly at Saul, to his embarrassment, although outwardly he remained unmoved.

"I speak the voice of the Sanhedrin," said Caiaphas, breaking the silence, "when I say, Saul."

"So be it!" cried the members in one voice.

"This is such an important undertaking that I will not enter upon it, unless I am given letters of unquestioned authority and credit to carry on the plans, even in Damascus," said Saul.

"It shall be so," said Caiaphas. "The scribes will prepare the letters and you shall have such force as you want to take from here, with such help from the other cities as you may need."

"Then I will go," said Saul. "I must leave in the early morning."

CHAPTER XXIII

TESTIMONY OF NEIGHBORS

Before it was yet day Saul rode out through the gates of the city with the ten selected guards from the Temple and equipment on donkeys for a journey of eight days. The guide in charge of the animals was familiar with the roads leading through the cities of Palestine to Damascus. Saul, having heard that there were many proselytes in Shechem (in the speech of his fathers), ordered that the first stop should be in that city. The guide protested against trying to reach Nablus or Shechem, a journey of fourteen hours, on the first night, because he said it would wear the animals down at the very beginning; but Saul said it was necessary for him to reach Shechem during the night time.

Even though arriving late, Saul aroused the leading men of the synagogue in Shechem; and from their report he was able to seize six men in the early morning and start them back, under guard, to Jerusalem. He then turned aside to Nazareth, whence had come the man who was the cause of this uprising.

In the squalid city he found no one sufficiently active to attract his attention. Even the rabbi seemed too dull to give any information; but anxious eyes were watching him from behind doorways, as Saul rode down the principal and illy kept street of the little city.

In Tiberias Saul was told that many travelers, who appeared to be fleeing in haste, had passed that way a few days before. The only people he could find in the city who avowed themselves followers of the Way were a caretaker of the synagogue and a half-witted shoemaker, proud of the distinction of being sent to Jerusalem.

In Capernaum the rabbi himself told Saul that the young man Jesus had been among them for many years, a gentle-mannered man, attracting many by his sincerity.

"We accepted him as a man," said the rabbi, in reply to Saul's question about any followers of Jesus. "So clean and wholesome was he, so intimately and sympathetically did he enter into our everyday life in acts of kindness and helpfulness, that we failed to note that he had any followers, except a few companions who hung on every word he uttered. He did not seem to us to be teaching a new religion so much as urging men to carry out in their lives the things that all of us know to be at the foundation of our own religion. We cannot believe that he taught any dangerous doctrines."

"Let us forget this man Jesus, since he no longer can teach," said Saul, in an effort to avoid discussion. "Have you not seen fugitives from Jerusalem, passing this way to Damascus?"

"Now I do remember quite a company passing through, just yesterday," replied the rabbi, raising his voice so that it could be heard by a young man who was listening intently. "They were inquiring where they would strike the road to Tyre."

While Saul set off impatiently, at the head of his company, the young man who had heard the conversation with the rabbi left the village on horseback, by a goat path which was a shorter route to Caesarea Philippi. Saul had led his company several miles on the road to the east, toward Tyre, when he met a caravan on its way back from the seacoast to Damascus. The man in charge of the caravan assured Saul that he had not met any travelers on the way, but that all the travel was toward Damascus. Fretting over the loss of time, Saul turned back and was for pushing on to Caesarea Philippi without stopping; but the guide convinced him that their badly jaded animals should not be crowded.

In the early morning they set off for their next stop, at Caesarea, for Saul had heard that there were many of the old disciples of Jesus in that locality, because he had once taught there. Their way led them down to the well-watered valley of the Jordan, through luxuriant growths, of which lower Palestine could not boast. The wealth of the yellow wild mustard in bloom, the anemones and poppies in their brilliant reds and royal purple, and the rich green grasses clothed the hills and slopes gorgeously; the eucalyptus, oleander, and walnut trees, with here and there a grove of olives, made it a scene of beauty; and over all the old monarch, Mount Hermon, was watching. So intent was Saul on his mission of vengeance, so annoyed by the delays, that he had no appreciation of the beauty about him.

The ruler of the city of Caesarea was exceedingly gracious to Saul, and with the extreme hospitality of the East took the greatest interest in providing for Saul's comfort and the entertainment of his company. The young man from Capernaum had arrived ahead of Saul and was watching, as if listless, all that took place. As soon as Saul's company had followed the city magistrate away, the young man, mounted on a fresh horse, left hurriedly toward Damascus.

"Your animals look so gaunt that I will have my own herdsman take them to my best pastures," said the magistrate, "and they will be fresh on the morrow."

"They need it badly enough," the guide grumbled.

"But will we be able to get them for an early morning start?" Saul asked, anxiously.

"My own stock will be with them, and in years my herdsman has not failed to bring them in at break of day," replied the magistrate.

Saul quickly inquired about any fugitives from Jerusalem.

"Now I do remember that several families passed through here a few days ago, on their way to Damascus, but they were so poor that I paid little attention to them," said the magistrate. "You should see the rabbi."

After a meal, prolonged by the magistrate's excessive hospitality until late in the evening, Saul was able to see the old rabbi, who plead that he would have to make the interview short, because in his old age he went to bed early. The rabbi was so uncertain about the people he had seen passing through the city that Saul could get no information out of him. He admitted that he had known the man Jesus at one time and had heard him several times, talking to small groups of people.

"He was a fine young man," said the rabbi, "tall and strong, and always in good humor, yet he never uttered an idle word. He was about your age, but his face was free from care and inspiring to look upon. We liked him very much and his influence upon our young men was for the very best."

"Are there any of his followers here?" Saul asked.

"I hardly know how to answer that question," said the rabbi, apparently greatly puzzled, "for he seemed satisfied with telling people the things that helped them in their lives and was indifferent as to whether anyone became his follower. If you had asked me if anyone had been influenced by him in this city, I would reply that a great many had come under his kindly spell. I heard that he was killed in Jerusalem, and we who knew him could never understand why."

"His followers in Jerusalem are preaching against the Temple and seek to do away with the law," said Saul.

"Of course that is bad," said the rabbi, "for the Temple is a wonderful building, erected by Herod mostly for his own glory; but off here we have no Temple, and it would seem impossible to do away with the law, for the Sanhedrin makes so many new laws that no body of men could very well do away with them."

"I am almost of a mind to have you sent to Jerusalem for investigation," said Saul.

"Send me to Jerusalem for investigation?" The old rabbi laughed. "Why, son, I am entitled, on account of my service for my people, to question those who keep themselves in Jerusalem. You are beside yourself and only serve, in your madness, the men who live off the fat of the altar, while we struggle to get the necessities of life and pay our taxes to Rome and our tithes to the Temple. Go on your way, but let me alone in my placid, old age."

After most diligent search that night, Saul was not able to find any victims in Caesarea Philippi to send back to Jerusalem; nor could he find anyone who was deeply interested in his mission. In the morning he waited impatiently until long after sunrise, before the herdsman came in, who had a tale to tell, how in the night a bear, or some other wild beast, had come down and scared the animals so that they scattered in every direction. The magistrate gave the herdsman a scolding and threatened him with punishment, if he did not bring in the animals of his guest. Saul tried to hire other animals, but it seemed impossible to find any for hire to go to Damascus. Late in the day the herdsman appeared with the animals, and Saul insisted that the guide should saddle to start at once.

"Leave me at this hour of the day?" cried the magistrate. "My name would be ruined. I would never dare to set foot in your city nor to go outside these walls. The Lord would look down on me in anger, woe is me! I want to be kind to the guest in my house and he turns upon me as an enemy and will not partake of my poor fare. Stay until the evening meal is ready and when you have eaten I will let you go, though I will never escape the curse of sending away a guest in the night."

The evening meal was lavish and the magistrate held Saul in conference until a late hour. Then Saul, deciding he must be on his way, aroused his company after much delay, so that he was ready to start at midnight. The magistrate was pleading with him to wait until the morrow, but Saul rode away in the night.

"Did the young man from Capernaum get a good horse?" the magistrate, with a sly twinkle in his eye, asked of his herdsman after Saul rode away.

"Aye, the best I could find in the city," said the herdsman.

CHAPTER XXIV

DARKNESS TO LIGHT

In the early morning, worn, weary, and dusty travelers, some riding, some dragging blistered feet, were coming into the groves and shady places of Damascus from their forced march along the sandy roadway. They cast anxious looks back over the plains and were happy that no clouds of dust disclosed their pursuers. For all along the road the day before, the young man from Capernaum had ridden, warning them that Saul was in pursuit.

They had fled to Damascus to escape the persecution of the priests of the Temple, to a city that was not controlled by the Jews. They knew that followers of the Way who had preceded them would open their homes to them.

Saul had climbed the hills out of the valley of the Jordan and was many miles behind the fleeing refugees. He had reached the plains leading from the slopes of Lebanon away and down to Damascus. He urged his company along with feverish haste among the rocks on the higher levels. He fretted at the delay for breakfast and rest for the animals. The guide was immovable, for he argued that he knew the long distance across those burning sands and that the animals had to rest and to be fed. When the journey was resumed Saul urged his horse on so fast that the guide came up with him and remonstrated.

"The sun will beat down on us across this plain, so that we will all be exhausted and our animals unable to carry us through," said the guide. "You must not try to go faster than I permit. Your horse is even now growing weary."

So slowly did they seem to move, notwithstanding hour upon hour of travel, that the great peaks of the Lebanons apparently stood as closely over them as in the early morning. The sun was high in the heavens and beat down in fierce, burning rays through the clear sky; the rocks along the way looked as if they had been scorched to blackness by the sun's rays, and the yellow hills to the east stood out as if they had been cast from bronze by the heat for sentinels of the desert.

The air quivered from the heat; in the distance, to the north, was a shadowy line of darker hue, marking the course of the Abana flowing down from the snowy Lebanons to the oasis of Damascus.

"Could we not push forward a little faster and reach water before nightfall?" Saul asked the guide.

"We will reach a good camping place, if we do not overdrive our animals," the guide replied.

While his horse plodded along, Saul raged over the slow progress and planned how he would carry out his campaign in Damascus. His life had not been spent in the hills; he missed the people of the city; the glittering wastes, dancing in the heat waves, oppressed him. The dulness he had found in the small-town rabbis and magistrates made him angry; the complaisant hospitality of the local people he had met irritated him. Their world was so small that they cared little about the results of great movements. Even the tolerance of Gamaliel came back to him as annoying, and he reasoned that he had done the right thing in going counter to such forbearance.

Saul felt disappointed in failing to send back more prisoners; but, he reasoned to himself, he would gather in great numbers of those fleeing to Damascus and stamp out the foolish teachings of the Way. He congratulated himself that in Damascus he would have them as the fowler held his captives in a net. He would bring them in fear to the judgment, begging for mercy, these deluded followers of the good-natured, misguided man of starveling Galilee. He urged his horse forward, leading the cavalcade. No breath of air was stirring; his lips were dry and impatiently he hurried on, when he heard the guide coming forward to check him once more. He felt that the guide, like all men and conditions, sought to restrain him. He was resolved to press on. No one should detain him.

The bright sun was instantly shut out. Saul's head dropped on his breast. He was falling from his horse just as the guide came alongside and caught him, so as to let him down gently. Others hastened up and lifted Saul's head, to relieve him. His face was bloodless. His open eyes were set in a gaze that seemed to the guards as if he were in a trance. For a little while Saul was immovable, his limbs rigid and cold; then he looked into the sky, over which floated a few scattered small clouds and, reaching out his hands, he strove to lift his head. His parted lips and intensely staring eyes frightened his companions. They lifted his head a little higher and propped him up with their coats. A Temple guard hurried up with a water bottle and sought to give him a drink, but Saul brushed it aside, holding up his hand in token of silence. All the time Saul's eyes were fixed on one spot where was floating a filmy cloud, to him alone a vision of ineffable love, shining into his eyes above the brightness of the sun.

Sitting up, without taking his eyes from the place in the sky on which they had been fixed, Saul called out in a loud voice:

"Who art thou, Lord?"

The guards heard only an unintelligible sound as if in reply, but Saul heard a remarkable message, a wonderful message, which he repeated over and over to wondering multitudes, to proud Pharisees, to barbarians, to scholars, even to slaves, to howling mobs, to rulers of the people, and sent it echoing along the centuries:

"I am Jesus, whom thou persecutest."

It was the stupendous event. From it flowed a new life, filled with the spirit of sweet reasonableness. Saul had been in the divine presence. He had seen face to face his Lord and Master. He had become acquainted with infinite Love.

He lay for a long time gazing into the heavens, after the vision had gone, as if by his concentration to call it back; but he knew from the revelation that he must go on his way and it would be told him what to do. He reached out his hand for help to rise and, being lifted to his feet, he found he could not see. His companions led him to his horse and helped him to mount. While they led his horse the rest of the way, Saul in darkness pondered the wonderful thing that had come to him.

In Damascus the word spread rapidly among the fugitives that Saul had come, but that he was helpless. A woman waited on him, but he would neither eat nor drink. For three days she heard him mumbling penitent prayers, and she heard him frequently repeating the name of Jesus, to whom he addressed his supplications as "Lord Jesus." She was one of the followers of the Way and hastened to tell a devout old patriarch, one Ananias, about it.

"I have heard of him," said Ananias, in reply to the woman's third report to him, "that he did much evil to the saints in Jerusalem, and that he came here to follow up his persecutions. Still I doubt him."

"You should hear his piteous pleadings to the Lord Jesus for forgiveness," said the woman. "He neither eats nor drinks, and he is blinded."

"Offer him food," said Ananias, "and, if he refuse it, offer him drink; and, if he refuse drink also, ask him what he would have. Ask him if he would go into a house of one who believes on the same Jesus. I will commune on the matter and wait your answer."

Ananias spent a long time in communion with his Lord over the question and knew that the answer was for him to go and lead the man aright.

"When I talked to him after the manner you said," the woman told him hurriedly, after she had again seen Saul, "he would not let me go until I led him into such a place as you would desire him to be. When I told him about you, he charged me if I loved my Lord, that I bring you quickly. He is so eager to hear you that he trembles in his anxiety, lest you may be delayed, and refuses drink and food until he sees you."

When Ananias came into the room, Saul, reaching out his hands gropingly finally touched the cloak of the patriarch. Seizing it, he pulled Ananias down by his side. Eagerly he grasped every word the kindly old patriarch spoke.

"But can he forgive me?" Saul cried out, after Ananias had told of the wonderful mercy that had been shown to others.

"He is Eternal Love, and I am sent to tell you about him and the things you may do, if you love and obey him."

Ananias gave the message as if every word were a precious jewel, to be weighed and valued by itself.

"With all my heart and soul and mind I do believe and will obey," said Saul.

"Jesus who appeared to thee in the way," said Ananias, rising and laying his hand on Saul's head, as if he were a child, "hath sent me that thou mayest receive thy sight and be filled with the Holy Spirit."

Looking up at Ananias, Saul found that the darkness had gone and light was everywhere. He followed Ananias and insisted on conforming at once to all ordinances which were required of other followers of the Way.

PART V

Meditation and Preparation

CHAPTER XXV

IN ARABIA

Under the kindly care of Ananias, Saul was refreshed and restored in mind and body. He spent days listening to the story, from the lips of the old patriarch, of the interesting life of the man and teacher, Jesus of Nazareth. Even the miracles which he had performed seemed to Saul more an exhibition of Divine Love than of supernatural power; at least, the end attained always seemed to be the one objective toward which all the teaching tended, love of fellow-men and of God.

Saul did not see in the miracles any doubt of the power necessary to perform them, but he marveled greatly that everyone exalted the principle of Divine Love rather than the display of power. From this he passed on in his contemplation to consider the personality of Jesus, and found that in his life there was not any demarcation between the display of this wonderful love and the claims of his being the one sent to win men back to the great fact that God is spirit and must be worshiped in spirit and in truth. He was astonished to find that the old truths contained the principle for which Jesus labored; only now it was clear to Saul that the narrow vision of men had built around the old truths insurmountable barriers, which prevented devout men from coming to a full understanding of the revelation of truth by the life of Jesus.

Saul, in his awakening, learned that these teachings of the Way set aside the casuistry of the priesthood;

that by this life given in humiliating sacrifice came the assurance of the resurrection, beyond the mere philosophical hypothesis of clever thinkers. The clouds were swept away by the simple story of that most interesting life; and men, untrained in logic, unlearned in the intricacies of legends, were able to speak with convincing power of the certainty of salvation and of life everlasting.

Ananias carefully repeated many of the teachings of Jesus, and Saul, with his life-trained memory, quickly rehearsed them and treasured them.

"Are there any records of his sayings?" Saul asked.

"No. Strange as it may seem to you, he gave freely of his spirit, but gave little concern to form," said Ananias. "We have his life, his love, his sacrifice, and his promise. Many of those who walked with him are or were in Jerusalem." Ananias paused, and in silence looked on Saul.

"Miserable is my life for the wrongs I have done, not knowing they were evil," said Saul.

"Grieve not, but rejoice that even now the revelation of the truth has come to you," said Ananias, with all the tenderness of forgiveness. "They will gladly receive you. I was about to say that those who walked with him are in Jerusalem, and we, who are so far away, zealously treasure any word he spoke. The time and place that he uttered a saying can be remembered, but it is his spirit in our lives that shows us the way to receive his promises and how to live close to God."

"Will you again tell me the story," said Saul, "that I may not miss any part of it?"

"I will gladly repeat it until you are sure you have all that has come to me, and just as I received it," said

Ananias, "but he did not give it as a formula.   He gave his life to redeem men."

Ananias did not weary in retelling the story, but Saul often interrupted to say that the revelation he had already received had made things plain.

A sweet peace came to Saul, such as he had never known.   His grief was absorbed in the revelation which he had received.   The mystery, the meaning, the magnitude of the manifestation, the revelations of power and of love overwhelmed him.   In deepest thought he tried to adjust himself to the marvelous simplicity of a love greater than the world had ever known.

The radical change in his viewpoint gave him anxiety lest ever again error should rule in his heart.   If worthy of such miraculous display, then, he reasoned to himself, he should devote himself to the spreading of the knowledge he had obtained among the sons of men. Heretofore he had dealt with such problems of life as depended upon his personal efforts to solve.   Now, there was a new question: the solution of the life here and hereafter, from the exalted plane of his direct contact with the Eternal One, who had given him the message to be carried to others.

Saul felt the responsibility that had come to him and, feeling that responsibility, he felt the need of being sure that he was a capable messenger.   Association with men who knew Jesus would not help, for his mission had come from a higher authority.

In solitude and contemplation Saul resolved to become a fit instrument for the boundless work.   He wrote and dispatched a letter to his family:

To Ben Hanan and Deborah, my beloved parents, from Saul, their son. The Blessings of eternal life be on you. I have had the most wonderful experience, which has changed my whole manner of life, but it is not possible to tell you in this letter from Damascus. I desire that in time you may know the great joy that has come to me and the life-task before me. Shortly I go into some out-of-the-way place which I do not now know, and will remain there for a period, the length of which I do not know; but rest assured that all is well with me. After such time as may be determined by circumstances and a power higher than we are, I will return to you. My former admonition to David is renewed. I would have you give my love, greater than ever before, to all the family and friends.

SAUL

After days of conversation with Ananias and those he found in Damascus of the Way, Saul joined a caravan for the peninsula of Sinai. The caravan turned aside from the usual route to deliver merchandise in the strange city of Petra, surrounded by sandstone cliffs and reached only by a tortuous passage through the clefts of the rocks. In times long past, temples and tombs had been hewn in the face of the pink-colored cliffs. The dwellers had little communication with the outside world, save as herdsmen came in from the surrounding plains and mountains, or when, on rare occasions, a caravan came in with merchandise. It suited Saul's mood to sojourn in this solitude, among these simple people.

Saul found among these strange people the relics of older religions and a mixture of many forms of worship. In their superstition they had adopted a few modern ideas that had come to them from the Greeks and from the schools of Alexandria so that it was not possible to say of what belief they were, nor to find any fundamental theory in their scheme of thinking. The sandstone walls

were an insuperable barrier to enemies and hid the city
from those who did not know the narrow entrance to
this isolated habitation.

He found that there was a good demand for tents and
immediately went to work at his trade.   He would often
spend much of the day in deep thought, such as to cause
the natives to fear that he was possessed of evil spirits.
One old man, an authority among these people, was
brave enough to venture into the workroom, while Saul
sat in one of his trancelike states, and to interrupt him.

"The man who thinks much to himself is either
dangerous to himself or has much to be forgiven; or per-
chance a great grief will rob a man of his interest in the
things about him," said the patriarch, Amur ben Hassen,
to Saul.

"I know that my ways seem strange to you," Saul
replied, "but I have much to think out and much to solve.
My griefs are past, but it will take me a long time to
readjust myself to a wonderful vision which I had; and
I have come here to think it all out.   Do you have any
confidence in visions?"

"I did not until I heard Philo speaking in Alexandria
the last time I was there," said Ben Hassen.   "He made
it plain that there are visions and dreams which should
be studied and interpreted, not by any rules of sooth-
sayers, but by meditation of the one to whom they have
come."

"Philo is a great thinker," Saul replied, "but he
seemed to me to spend much of his time trying to accommodate the Jewish religion to Greek thought instead of
bringing the Greek mind to accept the truth of the Lord
God."

"Then I take it your vision had something to do with your religion," Amur ben Hassen said, after a long pause.

"Some day I will tell you about it," said Saul. "Just now it is too sacred to discuss, until it has been interpreted, as you say Philo suggests. I wish I might have heard him."

"I expect shortly to have a copy of his work," said Ben Hassen, "because I arranged with a scribe to make me a copy and some day it will be here.'

"And what interests you so much in his work?" Saul asked.

"All my life I have tried to think out God," said Ben Hassen with the far-away look of a seer. "It seemed to me that Philo's work might help me. So you can now understand why it is that I want to become your friend."

During the passing days Saul found plenty of work to occupy his time. The glorious nights became more and more his hours of reflection. The clear air of the desert lifted him closer to the stars; the solemn stillness permitted the voices of meditation to become sweetly audible. He felt that the great walls surrounding the city were the walls of a new temple, in which the altar of sacrifice and ceremonials had been taken away, so that he could commune with the heavens themselves. Not only was he in harmony with the Psalmist who lifted his eyes to the hills whence came his help, but he lifted his eyes to the heavens, where dwelt Love, reaching out to him and to any man a helping hand.

His vision, the story told by Ananias, his years of schooling under the law, the ages of preparation of his people, the dark ignorance of the world outside the believers in Jehovah, the ritualism that had been satisfactory to him and which was sacred devotion to the great body of Jews, the bitterness and selfishness of all people, led him to the true conception of the deep significance of the life of the Son of Man. As the days passed, there grew in his mind a firm opinion and a spiritual conviction that there had been shown to the world the way for man to lay hold on the peace of mind that comes to him who knows that it is well with his soul and his God.

He had a curious experience in the course of his meditations. In the light of his newly acquired knowledge, he reviewed the trial of Stephen and the part he had taken in the martyr's death. He sought to make plain to himself that he had to bear a full share of the guilt. Yet the grace that had been shown him and the voices of his meditation banished any sense of guilt. He knew the wrong that had been done by him, not only to Stephen, but to the lowly and sincere followers of the Way; and, nevertheless, his exalted vision of the affairs of the new life forgave the deluded zeal with which he had acted, on condition that he would extend to others the same generous forgiveness which he had received.

In this soul-searching investigation Saul concluded that the scheme of love newly manifested among men was something more than kindness to men and forgiveness of wrongs; it was the very spirit of Jesus in the heart.

The mere physical life of Jesus was not of much concern to Saul; that was merely a man's life, but the spirit that so permeated every act of Jesus as to point to the Supreme Source of love fastened in his mind the authenticity of the claims of Jesus that he and the Father were one, renewing in striking distinctness the force and meaning of the midday vision. At times he was so filled with the beauty and simplicity of the truth which had flooded his soul that he was almost resolved to return at once and proclaim to the Jews in Jerusalem the things of which he had been a witness. When he visualized the misguided zeal with which he had urged the Sanhedrin on to action, he realized that he had represented the desire of others, and that he must prepare himself to the fullest extent to pass through severe trials and perhaps persecutions. As the days of his exile grew, so his inspiration led him to such lofty heights that he could not in words of common experience tell the wonders he beheld.

The old patriarch, Amur ben Hassen, would sit silently through long hours in the shop, while Saul worked and pondered, the highest and most delicate evidence of friendship. They sometimes walked at night to some of the lofty stone platforms against the face of the cliffs, where there had been, in ages gone by, altars of sacrifice. In the moonlight they would sit in silent communion, looking up to the star-bedecked canopy, as if they were priests waiting a voice out of the heavens. In a way they did hear voices, that is, they sought and found revelation.

Saul had told the story of his vision on the way to Damascus and had told Ben Hassen the purpose of Jesus among men, and what that life meant to the world; and Ben Hassen believed it, with the reservation that it all seemed so simple that it was hard to understand that God would do things with no greater demonstration of his unlimited power. The books had come and Saul eagerly and somewhat impatiently read them.

"Philo is only trying to build a system out of disjointed parts," Saul explained to Ben Hassen. "It is

as if he had taken a stone shaped for the Temple in
Jerusalem and sought to build it in with stones taken from
the Parthenon and the heathen pillars from Baalbek,
to make a substantial and beautiful structure. It is
essentially a man-made system. It lacks the simplicity
and beauty and perpetuity of the Divine Plan."

"I thought while listening to him," said Ben Hassen,
"that it was all very wonderful; but since you have told
me the other story my mind is not satisfied with it. I
wish now that I had the load of spice I gave to have it
copied. Still, his treatment of dreams is worth a great
deal."

"He shows that he never had any visions," said Saul.
"A man knows the difference between a dream and a
vision, and once a man has a vision he can so ponder on
it that great things will come. A dream comes when the
mind is lost in slumber and unloosed fancy jumbles the
impressions in unrelated connections. To depend on
the interpretation of dreams mixes the judgment of a
man with vain fancies."

Before Saul left Petra, Ben Hassen had become a
convert to Saul's teaching and in his own way taught the
new doctrine to his people.

In the solitude of the desert Saul had for two and a
half years pondered the great experience that had come
to him and the teaching he had received from Ananias.
He had readjusted his method of reasoning and life in
harmony with the revelations and the knowledge sacredly
committed to him. He returned to Damascus to take
up a new life, or rather, to live out a life that would be in
conflict with his former teachings, although he held it
to be a fulfilment of them.

CHAPTER XXVI

REJECTED OF MEN

Saul found it more difficult to get out of Petra than it had been to get in. After long waiting, he heard of a caravan which would pass on the main-traveled road on its return from the gulf to Damascus; and he was compelled to camp on the main road for several days to meet the caravan. Ananias welcomed him on his return, and immediately Saul plunged into the warmest controversies in the synagogues. Many followers of the Way held aloof from him, because they feared that it was a plot to catch them as prisoners for his persecution. While they could not question the soundness of his views, they could not at first believe that he had so changed as to be trusted.

In his boldness and new-found zeal, Saul sought to win the Jews to the new teaching. In the midst of his most earnest discourses some Jew would spit out epithets such as "traitor," "turn-coat," and "apostate." With patience and earnestness he tried to convince those interrupting him of the truth as he saw it. He was so well grounded in all the Scriptures and lore of the Jews that they were confounded when they tried to meet his arguments. He was winning many from among them to his message and relentlessly drove his opponents into corners, from which the only replies were taunts. His enemies became active in attending his meetings and spitting out—literally—their hatred upon him. His friends rallied to his side, for the followers of the Way had come to have the greatest confidence in Saul. His strong personality allowed no indifference to prevail; his honesty of purpose and fearlessness gathered around him devoted friends, or made implacable enemies.

After weeks of his activity the Jews determined to drive Saul out or to slay him. They went to the ethnarch, or governor, of the city with stories that this man Saul, who had been sent to take the followers of the Way back to Jerusalem so as to remove any danger of revolt, had, for some reason, turned traitor and was now a leader of the men who were stirring up trouble that would lead to revolt. They received authority to take him.

"If in taking this wild fellow," said the ethnarch, "it should become necessary to take his life in overcoming him, then your commission will free you of any charge."

"He may try to escape us, once he hears that we seek him," said the leader of the Jews who had come to make the complaint.

A slave in the household of the ethnarch was listening.

"In that case," said the ethnarch, "you may set watches at all the gates and I will send word to the captain of my guards to help you."

"Go to my captain," said the ethnarch, speaking to the slave, "and tell him strictly all I have said, and that the watch must be set at once."

The Jews immediately put their own men on watch and the slave hastened to deliver his master's message to the captain of the guard; but on the way he repeated the news to Ananias, who called a meeting of the leaders. They resolved that Saul should be sent out of the city at once. One of the converts, a guard, lived in a house on top of the city wall; and it was arranged that at midnight Saul should be let down from the guard's house by a rope outside the walls. In the shrubbery near a bridge a horse was concealed, on which he could make his escape to Jerusalem.

In the dark night Saul was let down outside the walls and found the horse and supplies. On his journey over the road which had been forbidding to him the last time he had passed that way, fretful and angry, Saul's thoughts now turned to peaceful contemplation of the world opened to his vision. The great distances now were small, in comparison with the sweep of his plans; the snow-crowned Lebanons, in their majesty, fitted in harmoniously with the magnitude and the message of Jesus. Saul found that the towns, valleys, and hills along the Jordan, familiar to Jesus, now emphasized, by their very ordinary appearance, the great love of man and the spiritual consecration of the Great Teacher, who sought men with hearts and souls, burdens and discouragements. While passing the place of the execution of Stephen, near Jerusalem, he recalled the gentle words of the martyr and saw anew, in a glorified halo cast by the setting sun, the rapture on Stephen's face when the executing priests were about to cast the fatal stones.

While his sister and Ben Gerber were warm in their greetings, they had an air of reserve which seemed to chill their reception. Saul felt that it was not the time to tell his story to them, that he came to win their hearts by his glad tidings and not through their pity for him. He hunted up the disciples, again meeting openly, and tried to join in their assemblage; but many, recognizing him, drew away in silence and fear. He told them of the great work he had been doing in Damascus for the Way and how he had been driven forth. Still they did not trust him. The cold manner of the disciples was anguish to his soul. He was going out of the synagogue, drooping with sorrow, when he felt a hand on his shoulder, and, turning around, he beheld the kindly face of Barnabas.

"I believe in you," said Barnabas. "Come with me and tell me all about what has happened."

In the house where many of the disciples were living Saul told Barnabas of the vision and the revelations, of his sojourn in Arabia and his experience on his return to Damascus.

"The time has come, Saul, for which I have longed," said Barnabas. "Now I can serve you and you can serve our cause. Tomorrow I will take you to Peter and James, that they may hear your story."

For two weeks Saul conversed with Peter and James, telling them of his vision and inspiration, as well as the message that he would deliver to the world. After listening carefully to all that Saul had to say, the apostles gave him their full approval and he began speaking in the synagogues. While the Jews were opposed to him, they feared to say much to him, because they knew that he might reply to them with the story of their part in the persecutions. They urged the Greek converts to Judaism, or Hellenists, and those who had returned to Jerusalem, to heckle Saul; and they even plotted to take his life. When this news came to the leaders of the Way, they urged Saul to flee, but he told them he would prefer to stay and meet whatever fate was in store for him.

They became so insistent that he believed they feared his presence would bring trouble to them. He appealed to the apostles, and they urged him to flee.

"I will consider until tomorrow," said Saul, "and then give you my reply."

In the early morning Saul went to his favorite spot in the Temple, to engage in devotions and meditation. He felt keenly the desire to send him away; it was almost a rejection by his friends of the Way. To him the Temple was sacred; it was a place set apart for worship; it was the outward expression of the hopes of Israel. The Law of Moses did not detract from the character and divinity of Jesus, but culminated in him. To follow the established worship was a privilege of a Jew which he felt in no manner destroyed his faith in the Messiah.

Saul appreciated the worship in the Temple and of Jehovah, as the highest expression of man's desire to know God. Neither then nor at any other time did he forget that as a Jew he was entitled to worship God, only he added that to him had come a closer communion with God. In such frame of mind he spent a long while at his devotions, seeking thereby to solve the question of whether he should stay and take the consequences, or follow the advice of his brethren of the Way.

With the bursting of the dawn upon the Temple there came to Saul a better understanding. If he stayed, he would stir up trouble before a knowledge of his purpose to serve faithfully had been fully established among the followers of the Way. If he left, in Tarsus he would receive the schooling of patience and learn the lessons of tolerance in meeting his own family and former associates. Then it came to him that his zeal had a slight touch of personal ambition, at least to the extent that he would gladly become a martyr, to no good effect. The time and place gave him a revelation of the spirit of sweet reasonableness with which he had been endowed and which he must show forth in his own life. In Tarsus not only would he learn to bear patiently the doubts of his own family, but there were those who were not Hebrews to whom he could tell the wonderful story, a story for all the sons of men.

Once more in his life Saul's vision cleared as if scales dropped from his eyes, for now it was revealed to him that he would serve a purpose in going back to Tarsus; he would be the bearer of glad tidings to the Gentiles. The dark doubts that had been in his mind because his brethren had urged him to leave were dissolved; and instead of banishment he would go out into a wider field—he now knew that he would be the apostle unto the Gentiles.

With spirits restored, Saul, coming down the steps to the outer court of the Temple, met the same priest he had scolded at the time of Stephen's teaching for being a listener to the teachers of the Way, instead of serving in the Temple. The priest felt encouraged to speak to Saul, on account of his noticeably jubilant air.

"These are early morning devotions," said the priest. "So early that those who will hunt you today would hardly expect you to be here."

"I am not fearful," said Saul, looking closely at the priest. "Would you report me?"

"I would protect you, since I know what you teach," said the priest. "As your zeal once excelled Gamaliel's, so now your faith exceeds his, or his when living."

"What are you saying?" asked Saul, grasping the priest's arm.

"Did you not know he died last year?" said the priest.

"I did not. Tell me about it," Saul urged.

"He seemed to have lost all interest in things and his body shrunk away. His funeral was peculiar, for he directed that none of the expensive preparations for burial should be indulged, but that it should be as plain a funeral as if he were the poorest man in Jerusalem. He even would not allow that a robe should be provided for him, but directed that the clothes he wore daily should be his shroud."

"I owe him much, but chiefly I would have asked forgiveness for thinking that he was too lenient with the men brought before the Sanhedrin," said Saul, mournfully. "He was a great and good man."

"He was so tender of the common people that he sought by his cheap funeral to shame the rich, in their extravagance. But hasten hence, enemies seek you." Saul looked at him questioningly and the priest added, "I am your brother, but I do not say much to anyone."

When Saul met the disciples that morning he told them that he was ready to go to Tarsus.

"I have come to trust in the ways of my Lord and Master," said Saul to the leaders. "The word has come to me that all is well with us. Henceforth I shall take these glad tidings to the Gentiles as well as to the Jews, for it has been revealed to me that, with patience in all things, I should wait the time and the season."

The disciples concealed him during the day and by night left the city to put him aboard a boat bound from Caesarea to Tarsus.

CHAPTER XXVII

LEARNING PATIENCE

Again entering Tarsus, after his years of absence, Saul felt the anguish of the years weighing down his heart. He returned once more unannounced; even the wharf from which he had often sailed reminded him of the hopes of his youth, gone forever; the family dear to his heart and hallowed by the observance of laws and traditions within its sacred circle would likely be, to some extent, embarrassed, if not alienated; then there were memories which he could not banish—his past was a part of himself which even divine power would not blot out.

Other passengers eagerly crowded ashore as soon as the cables were fastened, but Saul lingered, gazing with anxiety on Tarsus. So heavy was his heart, so keenly did he feel the disappointment he would be to his family and friends that it was only by a great effort that he resisted the suggestion of the captain of the boat that likely he would wish to take further passage. He marveled at this timidity as he wandered almost aimlessly toward his home. He had not known doubt nor hesitation when threatened with death in Damascus and in Jerusalem. He did not fear the scoffing nor the ridicule of the old friends among the rabbis in Jerusalem. But now, in the city of his youth, his feet stumbled as if lacking a mind to direct them on the way.

What value would all his rich experience have to those who could not be made to understand? No doubt, in kindness, his family and friends would bear with him;

even now he plainly saw that they would not really hear
what he had to tell them.   How could he offend the love
of his people by breaking with them ?   Then, as he neared
the familiar street leading to his home, his soul cried
out in agony for more of the spirit of sweet reasonableness with which to do and bear his part until the fulness
of the time.   He found himself lacking in the application of the faith in his heart to the everyday life.   In
alarm he found himself almost doubting the efficiency of
the love newly revealed from on high to stand the trials
of life.

The years had brought changes in the appearance of
Saul.   He was now in his thirty-fifth year, and, in the
reckoning of the calendar adopted at a later time, it was
36 A.D., making him about five years younger than Jesus
of Galilee.   The intense emotions to which he had surrendered in the loss of his wife and children;   the fierce
zeal with which he had plunged into the drive against
the followers of the Way;   the shock with which he met;
his days of meditation;   the long period in Arabia—the
sunburning there and the sunburning on his trips across
the deserts;   the great earnestness with which he had
entered the work of teaching the new Way in Jerusalem;
the great disappointment he felt at being urged to retire
to Tarsus—all these had left lines on his face which in
other men would have represented many years of active
life.   His beard now covered his face, and his hair was
beginning to grow thin on his forehead.   Those peculiar
eyebrows had grown heavier;   while his eyes had not lost
their luster, they had a steadier vision and seemed to be
looking into the very depths of the human heart, in
tenderness and in sympathy.   The heavy lines of his

face told a story of suffering, his eyes showed the hunger of his soul for companionship.

He found his brother David in the booth, who, in his young enthusiasm, threw his arms about Saul and gave him welcome. In the workroom his father was superintending the craftsmen, of whom there were several. Ben Hanan looked Saul over carefully and then gave him hearty welcome.

"I knew that you would return," said Ben Hanan. "Go in and meet your mother."

"My son, my son," Deborah exclaimed, hysterically throwing herself into his arms.

It was a long time before conversation was begun. The mother would not listen to anything from him until he had gone to a room she had kept waiting for him. There were his garments which he had left three years before and some of the things Tabitha had made for their home. He felt all the loss of her; his love was as great as ever before, but in his soul was a peace that quieted lamentations. David had taken up his home in the house Saul had built and he hastened to offer Saul rooms in it.

"It is as I wished," said Saul. "You continue to use it."

The family gathered for the evening meal and Saul told the story of his life since he had been away. The ominous silence of Ben Hanan, the quiet and unquestioning way in which the family listened aroused Saul to give more details.

"Has not this any interest for you?" Saul exclaimed.

"Much more than we show," said Ben Hanan. "You are of this family and we will do all and bear all for your sake, but we had heard much of this before you came.

Your place is here among us, but we have the right to urge that you do not bring shame upon us because of your beliefs. At least, I ask that for a season you refrain from making these statements in public, here in Tarsus. You have spent much time in thinking over your experience; now take some time in meditation and life-restoring activities."

"What I propose to do, that I must do," said Saul, "but out of regard for you I shall abstain for a while from any discussion; and, if it would be better, I may leave, to avoid any feeling of shame to you."

"I could not endure you being driven forth," said Ben Hanan, noticing the tears in Deborah's eyes. "We had resolved to make you happy in this home, if such can be; and to have you with us for our consolation. Your mother has grieved much about you, and age has come upon me. David is now more efficient in the business than ever I was."

"I have not neglected the commandment to honor my father and mother," said Saul, "and I will do all I can to make your life pleasant."

"Bravely spoken, but I can see that your heart is set on other things." Ben Hanan spoke kindly. "Ben Arza is so feeble that he needs some help; and at least you could give him aid in teaching the young, out of regard for the years he spent upon you. Such work may help you in coming back to a reasonable view of life."

"I would not have you think that I have become an apostate," said Saul. "I can believe all that I was ever taught and follow every law and rule I ever learned; still, I now know and believe this other wonderful explanation of life and our purpose in history. I promised you on our first trip to Jerusalem, out there in the hills, that if ever I thought I learned the great meaning of our long and strange history, I would bring it to you for your thought. I will remain for a season and it may be that you will consider what I have said."

"Then, the Lord be praised, you are not an outcast," said Ben Hanan, "but there is yet a chance for your mind to become normal."

In private talk with David, it was agreed between him and Saul that no further word would be spoken to their father about the matter until the father opened the subject. Ben Arza had grown old rapidly and he was glad to have Saul to help him. When Saul wanted to tell him about the Way, the old rabbi said: ·

"Not now. My days are too few. I have heard about you, but I could not argue with you and I would not listen. I am living along through these days because I have lived the same way all my life, and shortly the end will come. I am now ready."

Among all his former friends Saul found a barrier against any discussion. They showed him great love and, by concerted action, treated him as if his mind were not sound, as if it were agreed that no one should permit him to tell his story.

There were many Greeks who had accepted the beliefs of the Jews and who gave allegiance to the idea of Jehovah, but they had refused to submit to the ordinances and customs of the Jews; and they were commonly called "God-fearers," sometimes called "Hellenists," although the more strict use of the latter term designated those Jews who had been born abroad and who had remained true to the faith, while having adapted themselves to foreign customs. Some of the "God-fearers," having heard of Saul's experience, sought opportunities to talk with him secretly. While willing to tell them the story, Saul felt keenly the slight being put upon him, even by their desire to hear him secretly. He chafed under the good-humored tolerance with which his own people laughingly dismissed any reference by him to his experience. Opposition he could dare, argument he could meet, but ridicule was unendurable. It was undermining his great earnestness; it was chilling his soul; it was destroying his sense of proportion.

For a considerable period of time Saul took up the work of making tents. He found himself restored to his faith in himself and in his new cause, while planning for action. After many days of silence he began teaching for Ben Arza, but he shrewdly observed that the old rabbi would seem to sleep, while the classes were being heard and instructed; and yet, when he awakened he was alert, as if he had been pretending sleep. He wanted to revolt against this concerted suppression of the subject nearest his heart, but he accepted it as a part of his schooling as a fit messenger to those who would not hear, although they had ears. So faithfully did Saul work at his trade, so silent had he become, that Ben Hanan was worried.

"What did Gamaliel say of these people teaching the Way, as you call it?" Saul's father asked, after some months had passed.

"He advised to leave them alone, and let it appear whether time proved them right or wrong," Saul replied.

"That was a wise conclusion," said Ben Hanan. "It is unfortunate that you did not follow his advice. Then you would not have become so wrought up as to lose your calm judgment, when you had your stroke on the way to Damascus."

"I felt that Gamaliel's judgment was so conservative, so finely balanced," said Saul, with feeling, "that he could not see the danger to the Jewish faith. Now I am convinced that he saw the truth as I have come to know it, but did not have the courage to embrace it. Much learning had made him uncertain of his ability to discern the truth."

"Did this man Jesus leave any book of prophecies?" Ben Hanan asked.

"His was not a life of writings, but a life of revelation of the Divine Spirit," Saul answered.

"Now that you think over all the events," said Ben Hanan, "do you not think it strange that one who was to be the fulfilment of prophecy should fail to announce himself to all of us, so that there could be no doubt that he was the One looked for?"

"He did that in the divinely grand way by coming as a man, thereby forever appealing to men," said Saul. "He was a man, even as I am, and made manifest God's love of man, as well as the Infinite Grace by which we may become joint partakers of eternal life."

"But what will happen to men in their moral relations, if they are once led to believe this new doctrine and rely solely on what you call grace, neglecting the careful living we enjoin under the law?" Ben Hanan asked as if it were conclusive.

"All that was required under the law as right living, and more, will be required of those who follow him," Saul replied.

"You only now answer my former question," said Ben Hanan. "He left no writings and therefore no laws to be violated. You now see the absurdity that is so plain to me."

"All that is required as to a pure life by the law, and in addition a life so pure that the law could not define it, is what he left for our guidance. His spirit entering into our lives gives us a higher standard of morality than all the laws which were ever written. For that reason I can live in obedience to the law and yet not find myself satisfied with it; even having obeyed the Jewish law, I have greater inspiration from his life to do the right and just thing and strive to reach the high standard set by Jesus." Saul was about to continue when his father waved his hand in gesture to cease.

"Let us stop," said Ben Hanan. "I only ventured so much, thinking that in this time you would have returned to reason. Again let it be understood that the subject is a closed book in our household."

During this short discussion David had been very busy inspecting cloth close by, apparently indifferent to what had been said.

"I wish that you would go with me to the wharf, to examine some bales of cloth I am about to buy," said David to Saul, after the father had left the room.

"I heard all that you said," David spoke kindly to Saul when they reached the wharf. "You surely know that father has advanced so far in years and has had his whole life so wrapped up in your success as a rabbi that it is cruel to try to turn him aside from his fixed views. Look what it required to change you, and you are a young man."

"David, I cannot longer endure this kind but firm repression by the family and by friends against the expression of myself," said Saul, in an outburst of rage. "The people are laughing at me. They fiendishly enjoy smiling at me, as if I were half-witted. As much as I love father, I cannot help feeling that this galling treatment is his plan. I will not longer stand it. I cannot."

"And yet you have taught in the synagogue and still observe the law," David urged. "Why not show your confidence in your belief and in your message by waiting the proper time and occasion?"

"You speak with wisdom, David," Saul replied, "but this message must go to all people, and I feel that I am set apart to carry it, at any cost. You do not reach the height from which I am looking."

"All that you have said appeals to me," said David, "and I have a plan that will prove my word. The business has grown because I have encouraged the people of Cilicia to exchange their cloth and their products for our goods made up, which they take farther into the country and sell. If you would go out over the country on business for the house, you would get away from here and have a chance to travel."

"The plan suits me," said Saul.

"One thing, it seems to me, you should have in mind," David urged timidly, "and that is to talk to a few men in each place privately about your message, until you have established a belief in their minds; and, by reason of their influence in the community, they will aid you in reaching others. You depend too much on your ability to speak in a crowd, and it would seem to me that you would profit greatly by being able to convert men in personal contact."

"For the present your plans are good," Saul replied, as if resigning himself to the inevitable, "but when the time comes, I will go out unhampered by business."

"Then I will manage it with father," said David, "but you must bear in mind that this is business and I hope that you will be able to show such results that you may be kept at it."

A few days after the conversation between Saul and David the booth was crowded with men who had come in with cloth and raw material to sell and exchange. So many had come in at one time that David found himself oversupplied, and other merchants profited by getting some of the trade. The people came without any warning and would not be able to return for several months.

That night David proposed that Saul should be sent throughout the province of Cilicia and even to cities outside, to make contracts for the purchase of supplies and the time of delivery, and to enter into agreements of sales of the product and time of delivery.

"Those people will never sell until they have come to market," said Ben Hanan.

"Even if they would not make final sale at the time," said David, "still it would increase our trade and avoid such a glutting of the market as we had today."

"But Saul, could you give your attention to the business?" Ben Hanan asked the question, implying his doubts.

"I would try to do so," said Saul, very humbly.

CHAPTER XXVIII

A BUSY SALESMAN

Saul, being equipped with a riding and a pack animal, went forth on his journey as a merchant. The reputation of the house established by Azel was so fine that he was able, in the nearby towns, to make a good showing of business. David wrote him to continue his tour, for his results were satisfactory; and, having gone to more distant places, Saul was able to make better terms. David wrote him again to continue; and, unless anxious to return, that he should not take the time to come back to Tarsus between his visitations to different centers, but might find some way of employing his time, if he had to wait for business. David assured Saul that they were well pleased with the undertaking, from a business point of view.

Thus it came to pass that Saul had many opportunities to talk over the great message that had come to him with men of the cities, and with the families that followed their herds and flocks from pasture to pasture. In the years that were passing he had grown so strong in influence with leading men that often he was persuaded to address the congregations of the synagogues in many places, or assemblies where there were no synagogues. He felt all the time that he should not make the spreading of the glad tidings his principal occupation, both because he was under obligation to attend to business, and because the time had not come to him in which to make a militant stand as the apostle to these people.

In many places small groups became so intensely interested that they asked how they could keep this message alive. Saul suggested the plan of organizing in the form of the synagogue government, as the simplest and the one with which they were familiar. He found many Greeks, scattered through the small settlements, who gladly accepted the message; and there were some reliable men, with whom he sat down to teach the words as he had received them. He traveled even out toward Damascus, but stopped in the mountains, where he was received gladly among a peculiar people who held to some of the heathen practices, making his labors very great, to keep them from grafting the glad tidings on the wild growth of their own religion. They wanted to ascribe the powers of divinity, as shown in the miracles, to their own god, to give the divine nature of the family, and especially the mother of Jesus, to their principal goddess. In his kindly disposed efforts to guide them aright, he met with the simplicity and persistence of superstition.

From this experience Saul gained a new knowledge of men, and he learned the great patience required to eradicate centuries of belief from the minds with which he had to deal. Not only was the experience helpful in his conception of the methods necessary to present the message so as to impress it upon the Jewish mind but it gave him a clearer view of the effect that the glad tidings would have upon the gentile world.

Saul told the people he brought into the new thought that they should seek every opportunity to confer with the men who had been with Jesus during his life, and told them the names of the apostles who could be found

in Jerusalem. Leading men were selected from time
to time to visit the apostles, to question them on the
message Saul had delivered, and they returned to their
own people with full confirmation of the teachings of
Saul. In like manner, there were men from Cilicia and
Asia meeting the teachers who had become prominent in
Antioch. The news spread slowly to Jerusalem that
someone had been doing a great work in the lands far
away from the large cities.

After six years of life among the outlying settlements
Saul returned to Tarsus. He had been successful in
the plan of establishing trade relations, so that now
David had enlarged the business. Saul was now trained
in travel and in meeting vicissitudes in the hills and on
the plains. He was as bronzed as any of the tribes
of the desert; he knew their lore, their lives, and their
hopes. He had learned that men of the great solitudes
thought deeply upon every scrap of knowledge that
came to them; that under the impulse of trade and
travel, opened by the government of Rome by its
wonderful roadways, there was an awakening of the
people from the lethargy of the Orient, which had
engulfed even the Greeks who had settled throughout
the region.

On his return to Tarsus, Saul refused to enter into
discussion with his own family, but went among the
"God-fearers" with his message. He did not at once
seek audiences, but he sought out individuals who had
influence and whose characters suited them as hearers
of his message. All the time he helped David to gain
a clear understanding of the new customers of the house.
Friendly Jews came to ask Saul questions and they

joined with the Greeks in learning the glad tidings as delivered by Saul.

The number of converts grew rapidly until the hearers sought to have Saul speak to the whole people, and they urged him to go to the synagogue. This he refused, saying that in any other place than Tarsus he would gladly do so.

Two years of Saul's teaching in Tarsus had brought about such changes that he now met regularly with converts who had observed the regulations and ordinances for full membership. At times he would conduct the Sabbath worship for Ben Arza in the synagogue, without any reference to his other teachings. Ben Hanan would sit on the bema with the council on such occasions, drinking in every word uttered by Saul, even if it were only the reading of the familiar Scriptures.

The father of Saul, now passing into the ripe old age of one who has spent an active life, could not understand the persistence with which his son clung to his new thought; and least of all could he understand how Saul, the rabbi, could be the leader of the Way. The dignity with which Saul carried himself, the tenderness he showed to all the family, the restraint he imposed on himself in any discussion of his teachings before the family, and the peculiar, peacefully dominating attitude with which he went and came so puzzled Ben Hanan that he yearned for the courage to speak boldly to his son, as of old.

There was something that kept Ben Hanan at a distance, there was a wide space of thought that separated him from Saul. Ben Hanan, curiously, felt as if he were

the youth and Saul the patriarch, to whom he feared
to disclose his questions, lest they seem ridiculous.

The little mother was not afraid of Saul. She did
not care for his doctrines—he was her son, there was no
other question worth while. David gave his sympathy
to Saul and his thought to the business, now growing
still greater. In a few words, he urged and encouraged
Saul to take more time for his converts, while admonish-
ing him to keep from discussing the subject in the
household.

While Ben Hanan was sitting in the booth one day,
watching the customers from distant places, an old
man came up to him and asked if he was connected with
the business.

"I have given my life to this business, which my son
now runs," said Ben Hanan.

"Then you are the father of Saul," said the old man.

"He is my son," said Ben Hanan, simply. "He has
taken up some peculiar, disturbing views."

"In that we differ," said the old man, warmly. "I
must see him before I leave, to have him settle some
questions which have arisen."

"Tell me how you can bring yourself to accept his
theories," said Ben Hanan.

"I can give you no better answer than to say that
the story he tells brings peace and hope into our hearts,"
said the old man. "You should be proud to have a
son who can bring so much joy to men. Out there in
the hills are men and women whose lives were bounded
by the hills and to whom there had been no hope. He
brought glad tidings that filled their hearts with love

and hope and faith. Instead of thinking ourselves outcasts, because we could not live obedient to the Law of Moses, we now know what is right and just and have the witness within us that we are right with God."

Ben Hanan did not reply, but he fell into deep meditation. He heard David tell the old man on his way out that Saul was speaking that night in one of the lecture-rooms in the Greek school.

CHAPTER XXIX

ANTIOCH CALLS

Saul was giving instruction to a large audience assembled in the lecture-room. After he had finished his discourse the meeting was open for general questions and discussions, according to the custom. Many had risen to give their views, and then the old man from the hills who had been talking with Ben Hanan spoke, without rising from his place on the floor.

"We have heard this message from Saul on the other side of the mountains, and I am directed to get his opinions on some questions, for our local government, which I will do privately. I speak now for another purpose. If you have a just appreciation of his ability, and if you place any proper value on the tidings that he carries to men, why do you either hold or allow him to stay in Tarsus? Why do you not send him forth?"

Before anyone could reply, a large man rose from the deep shadows of a farther corner of the room and made his way down to the front. Saul sprang forward to meet and embrace Barnabas, who had thus, unannounced, made his appearance in Tarsus. Saul told the people who Barnabas was, and that he owed his own acceptance by the apostles to Barnabas' kindly interest and help.

Barnabas, on being introduced, told the people of the wonderful work that had been done in Antioch. He said the work had grown so great that it was beyond the power of those who were leading to keep up with it; that word had been coming to the followers of the Way in Antioch and in Jerusalem of the wide distribution of the tidings by Saul.

"The time has come in Antioch when we must have a fearless and able advocate of our faith," said Barnabas. "While there is no persecution, yet influential men are criticizing us and many scoff at us. I have come to persuade Saul to work with us in Antioch, and I feel that the great occasion for which he has been fitted has come. The words spoken by our brother from the far country are almost a prophecy, at least they agree with the plans we had made in Antioch."

Instantly the whole assembly was noisy with approval. Saul alone was solemn and silent. While looking upon the audience, now wild in enthusiasm, he was thinking of the timidity of the disciples when he had returned to Jerusalem from Damascus, anxious to throw his whole energy into the teaching of the Way. The bitter disappointment he then felt, because they would not accept his labors among them; the fear they expressed that his former persecutions would be held against him and the faith by those who had suffered, all came back to him. They had not shown that confidence in the divine forgiveness which he had realized in his own heart. The joy of the crowd left him untouched. True, he reasoned to himself, he had received a vision in the Temple that had given him courage and faith; and, after all, he questioned if the work that he had been doing among the people was not a fulfilment of the promise that he should be the apostle to the gentile world. In a flash of the future and a rapid review of the past Saul felt that likely his idea of projecting himself into the famous work as a leader was not in the plan of his Lord and Master. Barnabas, with his keen sympathy, surmised the conflict in Saul's mind; and, gently laying his hand on Saul's shoulder, led him to one side.

"Speak what is in your heart," said Barnabas.

"I feel humble and thankful," said Saul. "Is this an appeal to my vanity or a call to sacrifice and duty? Will the brothers in Jerusalem still doubt me?"

"Would I make this journey merely to gratify your vanity?" Barnabas asked, with a searching look into Saul's eyes. "In the fulness of time all things work out the Divine Plan; and this is another step. Your years of growing faith and unselfish labor have fitted you for the place. I feel that I am a messenger of him who loved you."

Turning to the people, who had become quiet while waiting the decision, Saul said to them:

"I will go with Barnabas. My absence may put your love to sore test; but the years have gone by so rapidly that I must use every energy to make up for lost time by delivering this message wherever it can be carried. You must carry on the work at home, keeping the words I have delivered to you (as revealed to me) free from error, and in your teaching may the spirit of love inspire you. I must give up the joy and comforts of home and friends, to go whithersoever duty calls. Farewell!"

The people broke into lamentations and blessings. They had learned to trust him as one near and dear to them. In the shadows of the entrance the aged Ben Hanan hastily left, so that no one should see him. The old man from the hills came forward to speak with Saul and Barnabas and insisted on taking them to Antioch, since it would be a difference of only two days in his homeward journey.

Saul wanted Barnabas to lodge with him that night, but he had already agreed to lodge with an old friend from Cyprus. As Saul approached his home it seemed to him that, notwithstanding the night was dark, there was a warm glow of light about him, at least the shadows were lifting. When he entered the house, he was surprised to find all the family waiting. In his greetings were the cheery notes of youth, his eyes were bright, his movements were quick and strong.

"Father," Saul said, "in the morning I leave for Antioch. How long I shall be away I cannot say, but I am pleased to go, as well as to follow whatever course may be marked out for me. David, the business is yours, with only the burden of taking care of father and mother, which you would do anyway. Mother, always remember my great love for you. Now I must pack a roll for traveling."

"Not so fast, lest we have a word to say," said Ben Hanan. "While I do not understand what you teach, I have come to understand it is not harmful. We have not accepted your faith, but we have come to believe that it is no mere fancy of a disordered mind, as we thought at first when you returned. If it is true, as you say, then it brings a wonderful opportunity to men; and if it is not true, it does not make men sinners. While I have not the faith to believe what you teach, I have learned that your own soul is clean and strong. Even as you gathered yourself together and won the race, in your youth, when it seemed you had lost it; so now, notwithstanding my doubts, you have the moral courage and spiritual power to endure and perhaps to conquer. Our son, Saul, will always be in our prayers. Now make up your bundles, but come to us in the morning, even if we are asleep, and bid us farewell. For reasons which you understood I have not asked you to lead in the evening prayer, but tonight we wait for you to perform that service."

Saul was so overcome with emotion that he could only wipe away the tears; and, after a long wait, he threw himself on the floor, and, with his head in his mother's lap, repeated the prayer of his childhood.

CHAPTER XXX

RELIEF OF FAMINE

At the break of day Saul was fastening his bundles on the horse furnished by the friend from the hills, while Ben Hanan, Deborah, David, his wife and children, stood close by to bid him farewell. Saul clasped his aged mother for the last kiss and, straightening up, stood as if in a trance a vision had been given him.

"She waits for thee," said Deborah, smiling up in his face.

"Did you see her?" Saul asked.

"No, but I knew that you saw Tabitha," said Deborah. "You looked just like you did that morning, when you first left for Jerusalem, and she gave you the napkin."

The old man of the hills came up with the rest of his train, which Barnabas had already joined. They rode out of Tarsus toward Antioch. After days of travel they reached their destination. During the long days of that slow method of travel Saul's active mind swept far and wide and back and forth over all his experiences and knowledge, into the greatest depths and up to the dizziest heights of possibilities.

The unrestrained conduct of the mere pleasure-seekers, the levity of the Greeks, gave to the city of Antioch an atmosphere of insincerity. Being the capital of the province of Syria, it was the residence of many officials of Rome. It was on the Orontes, 15 miles from its mouth, and sailing ships came up from the sea in one

day. A nearer seaport was Seleucia, 5 miles across the
land. On the uplands 5 miles westerly from the city
was the Grove of Daphne, in which was a shrine sacred
to Apollo and Artemis, a resort for those indulging
unbridled passions—even a Roman general imposed a
severe penalty upon any soldier visiting the place. The
population of Antioch was principally Syrian, with many
Greeks, and some Jews, whose ancestors had settled
there in the days of Seleucus by whom they had been
granted privileges as merchants, who had always been
active in the commercial life while maintaining synagogues in which their faith and teachings were kept
alive. At this time the city was prosperous and had a
population of 200,000.

Agrippa I had followed the execution of James, the
brother of John and son of Zebedee, in Jerusalem, by
persecuting the disciples so that many fled to Antioch;
and there they had established a strong organization.
In the very midst of the lightness and frivolity there
were many earnest men and women who gladly accepted
the life and hope and faith of the glad tidings.

Saul plunged into the work with all his ardent nature,
well knowing that sensualism dulled many ears that he
wished to reach. Even the general indifference of the
mass of the people was mixed, cynically, with high-
sounding phrases of morality, as if it were a mark of
superiority for people to scoff at their own wickedness.
Among the learned (there were many who gave Antioch
fame among scholars) were those who subscribed to the
highest code of morals, but held that indulgence was
permissible to them because of their knowledge of higher
morals; they did not hypocritically hide their excesses,

but openly claimed the license of satisfying any desire that did not violate any civil law. The pliable character of the native Syrians was molded by the licentious Greeks of the city.

Saul presented Jesus in such heroic lines that he challenged the attention of many who had been indifferent; he brought to the consideration of even indifferent hearers a crashing realization of the sacrificial life of Jesus and that through him had come the fulfilment of the longings of the human soul through the ages. He gave to the people the promises of life through the abundance of the love of God as shown in the supreme sacrifice of Jesus. Without wasting time in argument Saul assumed that men were religious by nature, and that they sincerely in their spirit desired to reach the highest ideal. In his matchless style he portrayed the Christ as the Son of God who had as the Son of Man excelled all other heroes in the submission to humiliation that he might open the way for all men to receive life everlasting and live in the joy of striving for the perfection found in the Christ.

Saul did not proceed along lines of developing a theory, but he gathered truths together and hurled them as if they were thunderbolts. He met all the claims of teachers who had worked out a system of morals by declaring that one right with God, he who accepted and followed Christ, had the spirit of righteousness, and would know it, from which knowledge not only would the follower of Christ seek the lovely and beautiful things of life, but he would always be anxious to do and follow the right. Saul told over and over about the sweet reasonableness of Christ and how his suffering for men would hold those who believed in him in such strong bonds of adoration that they would not be led astray by selfishness or passion.

The power with which Saul taught gave a new zeal to the followers of the Way in Antioch and his restless spirit forced others into renewed activity. He organized the followers of the Way so that they sought and brought men into the meetings. His exaltation of Christ and his frequent use of the Greek name for his Lord and Master made the name, Christ, familiar among the idlers of the streets, so that jesters thought it rare wit to call the followers of the Way "Christians" in derision. Saul eagerly sought men, irrespective of their former beliefs. Jews there were in numbers who accepted his teachings and there were many Greeks who came under his spell. One there was, Titus, who followed the apostle through the years.

In the midst of Saul's activities, Agabus, so wise that he was called a prophet, came up from Jerusalem and told the story of the poverty of the brethren in that city. He said that a great famine was coming on all the land next year, as it would be a time of great drought, according to the cycle of years, following the present summer, in which there had been a shortage of rain.

"It is unfortunate," said Agabus to Barnabas alone, "that Saul is so popular here. He was badly treated in Jerusalem and will hardly feel like doing much for us, I fear."

"You do not know him nor understand the spirit of him," said Barnabas. "We will leave it to him."

At the meeting of the congregation Saul cut short his own address and called on Agabus to tell his story to all the people. After Agabus had told the story of impending

famine and the persecution which the followers of the
Way had suffered under Herod Agrippa, Saul made the
most impassioned plea his friends had ever heard, for
contribution to a fund for relief. The collection was
liberal, but Saul urged that a fixed amount be contributed
every week until it would be needed.

"They are the people who have made it possible for
this word to bring hope into your lives," said Saul.
"This is not the only persecution they have suffered.
I myself did all the hurt I could to them in the time
before I knew the truth. You are not rich, but every
week you may give as much as you can spare and when
the famine comes we will save our own brothers and perhaps the lives of many who do not believe as we do.
And why not? If we believe that Jesus gave his life to
bring salvation to us, we should give to save any life."

All that summer of 45 A.D. and during the winter, the
church in Antioch collected the funds and stores for the
relief in Jerusalem. It was along at this time that Peter
visited Antioch, and he was pleased to see the work that
Saul was doing. Early in the following summer the
news came of the famine, made acute by the short crops
of the year before. So zealous had Saul been in preparing for this event that all the leading men of the Christians insisted that Saul should be one of the messengers
to take the relief and Barnabas the other. Saul insisted
on taking with him the Greek convert, Titus. Barnabas
agreed with Saul, not understanding the larger purpose
in his mind. Not only had the "fulness of time" come,
but Saul had caught slight murmurings of Jews who had
become believers, that Gentiles were being admitted to
all the benefits of Christians, without observing the Laws

of Moses. He resolved that the Jews of Jerusalem should know not only that the Gentiles accepted the glad tidings but with Titus present it would be an evidence that Greeks who had believed were contributing to the relief of the brothers in Jerusalem in their time of distress.

There was great rejoicing when the three from Antioch brought the relief and aided in its distribution. Saul and Barnabas went up to the Temple often, and there was slight murmuring among the Jews of the Way that it was a wonder that Saul did not take Titus into the Temple, for he seemed to think as much of this Gentile as he did of the chosen people who had come out for Jesus.

Some of these complaints having reached Saul, with a heavy heart, he had a conversation with Barnabas about it.

"It seems that I will never be understood in Jerusalem," said Saul. "Even now they complain because I have brought Titus who is not of the circumcision, and I thought to show them the breadth of the love of Jesus."

"Let that pass," said Barnabas, "for Peter was as much opposed to Gentiles as any of them, and at Joppa he had a vision of a sheet let down from the sky filled with all manner of beasts, unclean under the law, and he heard a voice commanding him to rise and eat. He replied that he could not eat any unclean thing, and the voice told him that he should not call unclean what God had made clean. And the interpretation was that he should go unto the centurion, Cornelius, who received the Holy Spirit and was baptized by Peter. Now let us avoid raising the question here, but go our way."

"This confirms my vision and my mission to take the glad tidings to the Gentiles, first I believe that the Jews should always have the message, but the Gentiles should not be neglected," said Saul. "I feel the urge more than ever to do all possible."

"This question is not fully settled," said Barnabas, "but in due time it will be settled right. We have the authority of Peter, and you have the confirmation of your own vision, and that is sufficient. I wish I could persuade my cousin, John Mark, to go back with us. If it seems well I believe our work lies outside of Antioch, and I am sure that it is well for us to return."

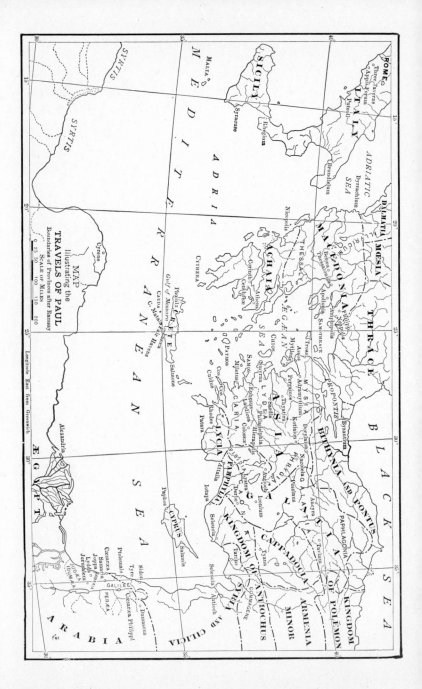

MAP
Illustrating the
TRAVELS OF PAUL
Boundaries of Provinces after Ramsay

SCALE OF MILES
0 25 50   100   150   200

Longitude East from Greenwich

PART VI
Herald, Leader, Martyr

CHAPTER XXXI

ANTIOCH IN PISIDIA

Barnabas had been at the head of the relief distribution, for Saul felt that his place was to act in such a manner as to attract the least attention to himself while in Jerusalem. When ready to leave, Barnabas received the grateful thanks for the relief given, and he expressed the hope that he and Saul would be able to make a journey through Cyprus with the message. The elders of Jerusalem thought well of the plan, and to their question why he did not go at once, Barnabas answered:

"We have gained great power in Antioch by earnest prayer of the whole congregation before we make a final decision, and then we act as a unit. This plan of work may take us to distant places, and we want all the help that can be given. We will lay it before the congregation."

Barnabas and Saul on setting sail for Antioch took John Mark with them. He had been in the confidence of the leaders in Jerusalem so that he had been carrying on the teaching of the Way, but he was sensitive to the doubt prevailing because he was a Jew with the rights of a Roman citizen. He was anxious to join in the journey through Cyprus.

Barnabas and Saul reported to their congregation in Antioch all that had taken place in Jerusalem. They laid out their plans of taking the glad tidings to Cyprus, and Saul urged that they should not return from that journey whatever the results, but they ought to have a free course to go unto other people, wheresoever the

Spirit or circumstances directed. He rehearsed his
experiences in Cilicia.

The Christians—they were now proud of the name
first applied to them in jest—after prayerful consideration approved the plan and provided the funds for Barnabas and Saul, accompanied by John Mark as helper, to
make the journey as far as they found hope and strength
to go. They solemnly anointed them as heralds of the
glad tidings to new lands. Barnabas and Saul, with
John Mark as their attendant, set out early in March,
47 A.D., for the port of Seleucia, whence they sailed to
Salamis.

The quiet and reserved manner to which John Mark
was accustomed, among the leaders in Jerusalem, was
in striking contrast to the nervous zeal shown by Saul,
although Barnabas bore it all in a tolerant way. Saul
seemed so anxious to land that he paced the deck of the
vessel, as if he were speeding the travel. He was now
forty-six years old. Strong, rugged, nervous, he could
brook no delay; kind, honest, fearless, zealous, he understood sympathetically before a speaker finished his
sentences. Words were poor vehicles of thought for
him, because they required time to utter and inade-
quately conveyed his meaning. His brain teemed with
plans, images, situations, arguments, possibilities, and
eventualities. While his face showed the suffering, the
deep thought, and the exposure through which he had
passed, his eyes were luminous with spirituality and his
kindly smile extended and invited sympathy. The
peace which "passeth understanding" had brought faith
and love into his soul. He walked, talked, and acted
as one inspired. His purpose in life was now fixed, and

he was pleased that the opportunity was presented for his great work.

They landed at Salamis, making their way through the towns of the island. Wherever they went Barnabas vouched for Saul, giving him credit by his own depreciation. The personality of Barnabas won friends to hear them and Saul charmed and convinced hearers. They reached Paphos, where Sergius Paulus, the proconsul, lived. Like all cities of any prominence, Paphos was overrun with teachers of necromancy, astrology, and dealers in charms. Against this superstition Saul hurled all his invective and arguments, attracting the attention of Sergius.

A certain Jew, Barjesus, had been gaining a livelihood from his magic and his pretenses of power, so that he had become a privileged character in the residence and at the receptions of the proconsul. Sergius Paulus, having sent for Barnabas and Saul, was listening to their explanation of their teachings, when the Jewish magician, Barjesus, at the side of the proconsul, interrupted by saying:

"This doctrine has been laughed out of Jerusalem, where they say it originated."

Saul turned on Barjesus with such awful anger that the sorcerer trembled from the knowledge of the falsity of his own claims. Saul exposed him to all present, closing his remarks with a curse that he should be blind for a season. In the presence of Sergius Paulus the sorcerer groveled and, begging for mercy, groped about sightless.

The issue of this incident before Sergius Paulus was twofold: The proconsul accepted the words of Saul graciously; and Saul took, from that time forth, his

Roman name, Paulus or Paul. Paul discovered that he had power greater than he had ever thought would come to him. He felt that it had come as a further witness to his mission in life; and that it carried an added responsibility that it should not be cheapened or lost in use for personal fame, but that it should be used for beneficent and holy purposes.

Upon the urgent demand of Paul the three men set sail for Perga, in Pamphylia. While John Mark did not openly protest, he urged a more leisurely trip back through Cyprus and then that they sail from Salamis. Paul closed the discussion by pointing out the delay. He urged that it was now the early summer and that soon the people would be leaving the low coast towns during the hot period.

It was possible to make the passage to Perga in one day, with favorable winds; but after they had rounded the western coast of Cyprus and had turned on the direct course, a little west of north, the wind died down. For a long time they made slow progress. Near midday a strong wind almost from the west drove them rapidly on their way. The wind increased to a hurricane by nightfall, while they were many miles from the Pamphylian coast. The sailors, struggling to hold the ship in its course, took in sail. All hands were lending whatever help they could give. The heavy seas washed the deck. Paul was helping to lash an extra spar, to prevent it being carried away, when an extraordinary wave swept him and the spar overboard. The ship righted and sped on its course in the dark. Search was made in the darkness, but he could not be found. The gale drove the ship to the coast.

All night long Paul was buffeted by the waves. Shortly after he had been dashed into the sea, he encountered the spar that had been washed overboard with him. He clung desperately to it through the long night. The storm abated in the morning, but the sea was still rough. His great strength was sorely taxed. Often the spar would be torn from him and he would have to recapture it. His friends were hunting for him, but failed to find him. In the afternoon a ship crossing his path rescued him, just when his strength was failing. His rescuers put back to the coast and found his ship. His companions rejoiced, for they had given up all hope of saving him.

Exhausted from his long exposure and terrific strain, Paul was taken to Perga, 6 miles up the Cestrus from its mouth. Perga and the coast of Pamphylia, in the summer season, were hot and forbidding. The inhabitants who could afford a trip were leaving, or about to leave, for the mountains of Pisidia, to escape the pestilential mosquitoes and the widely prevalent malaria. Thick swarms of mosquitoes enveloped Paul while he lay helpless. John Mark bitterly protested against staying in the miasmatic atmosphere and longed for the pure air of the Judean hills. Before Paul had recovered from his exposure he had a severe attack of malaria. Between the violent paroxysms of the attacks, Paul agreed that they should leave the low country at once, and urged that they should hasten into the mountains of Pisidia.

"You are not fit to endure the hardships of mountain travel," John Mark urged upon Paul. "Besides, if Barnabas and I come down with the same disease, we could not care for you. I am minded to return to Antioch and resume at a propitious season."

"The mountain air will give me relief," Paul replied, "and we should push on to Antioch of Pisidia. While this trouble will linger with me, yet I promise to be of as little burden as possible."

"I will not go on to certain failure," said John Mark, "and likely be a party to your death. If you will not go back with me, then I will return to Jerusalem."

"Go, if such be your cowardly spirit," said Paul.

John Mark turned back; and Barnabas procured pack and riding animals and equipment for their journey beyond the mountains. Often on the journey they had to stop while Paul suffered from the acute attacks of malaria, from which he would recover in a day. The attacks would come on him about every third day, in chills which shook his frame and an unquenchable thirst, followed by a high fever in which he would become delirious. He knew the disease from his experience among the people of Tarsus, and he knew that the poison in his blood would not yield to ordinary remedies.

Paul and Barnabas resolutely pushed over the high ranges, enduring the vicissitudes of their primitive method of traveling. Robbers beset the way. On one occasion a band of robbers was camped close to the crossing of a stream, where Paul and Barnabas were compelled to stay for the night. Paul and Barnabas made up imitations of bodies lying close to their camp fire, by spreading their extra robes over the rocks; then, wrapping themselves in their cloaks, they lay down a short distance away. They slept in watches. During the night the robbers came and were stealing up to attack the images, when Paul and Barnabas leaped upon them. The sudden attack alarmed the robbers, who surrendered their knives to Paul and Barnabas. Then Paul stood guard over them until daylight and plied them with the story of the Jews and his own experience. They gave a pledge, which even as robbers they would keep, not to attack Paul and Barnabas again.

In Pisidian Antioch Paul and Barnabas found a synagogue which they attended and, after being present one or two Sabbaths, they were called upon to give their message to those assembled. Paul had been suffering from his recurrent attacks of acute malaria, coming almost regularly every third day. A Greek physician by the name of Luke was called to attend Paul, and he became interested in his patient and in his teaching. The "God-fearers," at Luke's suggestion, came to the synagogue to hear the glad tidings, to such an extent that the Jews became jealous and stirred up the people against the travelers.

The heralds left the synagogue, to continue their work among the Gentiles. Then the Jews aroused the wives of the magistrates and other women of high standing, with stories that this religion was founded on a questionable birth of a man, and would become a disgrace to the people who were gathering from the surrounding country to hear Paul. A mob was gathered to drive Paul and Barnabas out of the city; the Jews joined in the persecution and drove the teachers out.

The travelers had been in Antioch of Pisidia for nearly three months, and had met people from other and distant cities. They had sent forth men so pleased with the new words that far in advance of them the news had spread, even to places the heralds would never reach. Yet the missionaries were driven from the city by a howling mob, threatening death and hurling stones after them. The friends of Paul and Barnabas, anticipating that such a condition would arise, had extended to them invitations to other cities. Tradesmen carried the news, so that there were many through the east, watching to give the travelers welcome.

While Paul and Barnabas were being driven out of Antioch, a driver of a caravan offered to give them passage to Iconium in his train; but Paul said they would first go to Lystra with their own outfit, because their journey would be frequently interrupted by the acute malarial attacks which would seize him, compelling them to wait a day until he would recover. The man with the caravan hastened on to Iconium.

CHAPTER XXXII

THEKLA OF ICONIUM

Onesiphorus, a shoemaker of Iconium, having heard many times about the man who had for years been traveling in the mountains and teaching wonderful things, was intently listening to the caravan driver telling about Paul and Barnabas being driven out of Antioch of Pisidia. The driver gave a detailed description of them and of the animals they had. He said he offered to bring them to Iconium but they said, because the smaller man of the two was sick at times, that they would have to travel slowly. The smaller man, he said, wanted to go to Lystra.

Onesiphorus set off at once for the place where the road divided, some 40 miles distant, to intercept the travelers and bring them to Iconium before they went to Lystra. He arrived at night where the road divided, one part leading to Iconium and the other to Lystra. He took his station by the side of a Roman milepost, where he stood so rigidly looking toward Antioch that he seemed to be a part of the monument. Late in the evening he wrapped his cloak about him, because of the chill winds from the mountains, for it was now November. A Roman messenger passing stopped to ask the large, silent figure if he were a guard or a bandit. Onesiphorus made no reply. During the night he rested by the side of the road, lest Paul should pass.

In the morning Onesiphorus refreshed himself with food from his sack, and drink from his water bottle, while his horse strayed toward a spring a long distance away. Statuesquely he watched the road from Antioch. Near midday he saw two travelers approaching, who answered the description the caravan driver had given. Paul was riding a small horse and Barnabas was walking behind a donkey loaded with their supplies. The dust of the highway enveloped them, so that they could not be seen distinctly. Paul was recovering from one of his attacks and his wan face was yellow from the sunburn and the disorder afflicting him.

"Are you not Paul and Barnabas?" said Onesiphorus, after greeting them.

"We are, and who are you?" Paul replied.

"I am Onesiphorus of Iconium, a shoemaker, and I come to urge you to bring your message to us. All night I have waited. My friends want to hear the tidings you bear. My house shall be yours as long as you will tarry with me."

"Such eagerness should be satisfied," said Barnabas to Paul, who wearily nodded his head in assent, and they journeyed to Iconium.

The shop of Onesiphorous was in a little court off from a side street. The wall of the house of Theokleia, a widow of noble family, was the boundary of one side of the court used by Onesiphorus. He worked under an awning in front of his living-rooms. The top of the flat-roofed house of Theokleia overlooked the court, immediately beneath a window of an upper room occupied by her daughter Thekla. Paul and Barnabas established themselves with Onesiphorus. Paul immediately began tent-making, while Barnabas looked after the affairs of their mission. They held forth in the synagogue on Sabbaths and many came to talk with them in the shop.

Thekla, who was engaged to be married to Thamyris, a wealthy young man of noble birth, was in a hammock on the roof of her home one sunny afternoon; and she listened closely to Paul, explaining his teachings to men while he worked. He was telling the men that the hope of a life eternal and the living of a clean life, full of acts of kindness, after the manner of Jesus, were the simple requirements of those who would believe and accept the "glad tidings"; that the resurrection was a fact. A Greek asked if this included women. Paul explained that Jesus included women in every part of his life, because they had immortal souls. Thekla was stirred by this statement, for only that day she had had an argument with her mother about Thamyris being a regular visitor to the house of Aspasia, the brilliant dancer and leader of the public women of questionable character.

"A wife should not be foolish," Thekla's mother had said. "Thamyris is too well bred ever to bring Aspasia into his home, and the home is your world. What your husabnd does outside of your home should be no concern of yours."

Thekla spent day after day at her window, listening to Paul and Barnabas, teaching all who came into the shop of Onesiphorus. She refused to come down, even at the request of Thamyris, for she had heard strange things, that opened her eyes to larger and fuller life. Aspasia had come to the shop to have some work done, and from her screen Thekla had seen and heard her. After listening to Paul telling the story of forgiveness of the woman whom the Jews were about to stone, Aspasia tearfully asked if such as she, who danced in the nameless orgies of the temple of Artemis, sold herself to the nobles,

yet abhorred the life, could have back the peace of her
earlier life.

"To you now, as to women during his life, he brings
the hope of the new life, and forgiveness if you obey and
follow him," said Paul.

"I dare not hope," said Aspasia. "I am the toy of
nobles who strive more to please me than they do their
wives, yet my sex revolts."

Thekla, from timid, unquestioning obedience, grew
defiant in disobeying her mother's commands to cease
listening to the strangers. The possibilities that through
this teaching would come a new vision to the women of
the East thrilled Thekla with a longing to help her sex.
The lofty purity of Paul's teaching, the beauty of the
Christian life, inspired her to seek more knowledge.

Thamyris and Theokleia agreed that the man Paul
must be driven out; for Thekla had already twice
refused to marry Thamyris on an agreed day. Thamyris
met a grain buyer from Antioch, who told him that the
Jews had driven Paul and Barnabas out of that city.

The winter months were past, and again Thamyris
urged Thekla to fix a day that they would be married.
She refused. He tried to divert her mind from interest
in Paul's teaching by taking her to a special celebration
in the temple erected to Artemis. The dancers circled
about the altar in wild and graceful figures; the priest
was gorgeously arrayed; but she saw Aspasia and her
dancing girls waiting back of the pillars, in hiding, when
Thamyris insisted that it was time for her to go, because
the dancing to follow would be given by the hetairai for
men, and it would not be proper for honorable women to
be present.

"Then the services in this temple are so vulgar that you would not have me see them?" Thekla asked.

"It is according to the customs of the ages," Thamyris replied, in a tone of finality, "and it will continue, even if some rail against it. Our people resent the maudlin sentiment of this meddler, Paul."

"Sneers will not destroy the hope he gives," Thekla said.

"There are only two kinds of women," said Thamyris, mockingly. "One is the hetairai, who never dare think on purity; and the other is the matron, who must not think on impure things. We safeguard our civilization by keeping the two classes separate."

"Not to safeguard, but to gain the license you allow to men," Thekla replied, hotly. "Your hetairai, from their knowledge of men, gain freedom of expression and access to knowledge; while you reserve for your homes the dull morality of satiated passion." She left in such anger that Thamyris did not dare to offer to accompany her.

The complaints of Thamyris to the magistrate, an officer of local selection permitted by Rome in the far eastern cities, that Paul was casting a spell over the women of the city, to keep them from marrying, caused an order to be issued for the arrest of Paul. During a banquet in the Roman style, given by Aspasia, a clamor arose in the street below, as she reclined at the table, holding a goblet of wine, from which Thamyris was sipping. She leaped from the table-couch and laughingly ran to the window. In a moment she screamed in fright. Thamyris, hurrying to her side, saw officers leading Paul and Barnabas toward the jail, followed by a shouting, hooting mob.

"I had that done, to stop Paul from turning the
heads of our noble women," said Thamyris. "He cast
spells over women, making them believe they have the
same right to think as men. Now he will not fool
them any more."

"You bigoted fool," Aspasia cried, with tears in her
eyes. "Your lust is your guide. He does bring hope,
even to me, and only a high-bred brute would do as you
have done."

Thamyris laughed in her face and playfully took her
in his arms to carry her back to the banquet table. She
turned on him like a wild animal at bay; and, in a torrent
of words, set upon him, striking and scratching at his
face until he fled; then, in her rage, she drove her guests
out of the house.

The news spread rapidly that Paul and Barnabas
had been placed in stocks in the prison. Thekla heard
Onesiphorus telling his friends what had happened; and,
although he lowered his voice, she heard him say that it
was done at the behest of Thamyris. That night she
bribed the porter of her mother's house with her bracelets
to let her out of the house; and in like manner she bribed
the jailor with a silver mirror to let her into the jail.

All night long she lay at the feet of Paul, who,
although cramped by the cruel stocks, told her the glad
tidings in his most interesting manner. In the morning
Thamyris and Theokleia hastened to the prison at the
break of day to take Thekla away. She refused to forget, or to cease her interest in the things Paul had
taught. They took her before the magistrate, with
whom they had made arrangements, and he threatened
her with proceedings. She calmly told him to proceed.

Nonplussed, they took her home, but her sweet patience and firmness balked them in all arguments.

That day the officers led Paul and Barnabas to the city gates, while a mob followed, pelting them with small stones and striking them with sticks. Thekla, from the window of her mother's home, in which she was a prisoner, watched in grief and anger the expulsion of men who gave higher hopes and better courage to the people. Then and there she resolved that under no circumstances would she wed Thamyris.

In the passing days her mother, the family of Thamyris, and friends tried to change her mind. They even brought a sorcerer, who claimed he could undo the spell which Paul had cast over her; but she insisted that there was no spell, that she was merely awakened to the fact that she had a soul, and had a desire to tell to others the story of the soul and its rewards.

After many days, Theokleia and Thamyris were advised by the priest of the temple of Artemis to let Thekla escape, then Thamyris should overtake her on the plains and by force make her submit to his passion, thereby breaking the spell cast by Paul. Her mother made life unbearable for Thekla and contrived to allow her to escape, under the impression that if she would go to Antioch she would meet Paul. Thekla fled with her own maid, hoping to find Paul in Antioch of Pisidia. Thamyris, pursuing, overtook her on the plain, to carry out the brutality advised by the priest; but her strong will, saintly purity, and newly awakened soul consciousness made him desist, and she journeyed to Antioch.

In Antioch the people were gathering for a great festival conducted by Alexander, the high priest of the native religion, in honor of the Roman governor, who was visiting the province; though Queen Triphaena was still recognized as participating in at least the honor of governing the land. Games, parades, and many forms of entertainment would be given in the arena. Thekla, coming into Antioch at this time, met Alexander, who thought she was one of the dancers, because (according to the custom of her country) she did not wear a veil. In greeting her he tried to kiss her against her will, as he would any dancer. She fought him, knocked off his priestly hat and scratched his face. This so enraged Alexander that he took her before the governor, on the accusation of sacrilege; and the governor, forthwith, condemned her to be offered to a lioness and to be exhibited as a victim in the parade.

She asked if Paul were in Antioch, but was told that he had not returned. Then she declared before all the people that she was under a vow, on a mission of "the God." The women set up such a cry when she said she was on a mission that Tryphaena, the queen, took pity on her and became responsible for her, so that she would not be subject to the brutality of the soldiers—a license, by custom, gave them the women victims for their lust.

Tryphaena, both from the high character of Thekla and from a dream about her own deceased daughter, of nearly the same age, became enamored of Thekla. The next day Thekla was produced and was compelled to ride in the parade on top of a cage, in which was the only lioness which Alexander had for the festival. In the parade were elephants and bears and all the entertainers. Among the dancing girls, on a wheeled platform repre-senting a bower, was Aspasia, who was surprised at seeing Thekla so situated. At first she gloated that Thekla had been brought so low; but when she saw that the cage carried a banner inscribed with the word, "sacrilege," her heart filled with pity, for she knew what fate awaited Thekla. The lioness reached her tongue through the bars and licked Thekla's bare feet during the parade.

After the parade Tryphaena again took Thekla, until the time she would be required, and spent the night listening to her story of the great mission she wanted to undertake, in carrying the glad tidings to the women of Galatia and of the East. Tryphaena refused to give Thekla up to the soldiers, who came for her the next day, and would not surrender her until Alexander came in person, with orders from the governor.

Thekla was led to the arena, stripped of her clothes, and wore only a cincture, which was required by Roman law to be furnished to any such victim. The audience had forgotten its sympathy of the opening day for Thekla and now howled for the sport. She was led to the gate of the arena by Tryphaena and there the guards took her and bound her to a stake, in front of the crowd, who howled with delight. Thekla sagged down on the thongs, shamed and hopeless. Then she spoke a prayer, in a low, clear voice, with such feeling that a solemn stillness settled over the wild audience, now eager to hear the words, the cry of her soul:

"My Lord and my God behold me, the shame of women is uncovered in me, and I stand in the midst of all the people. Remember me in this hour."

Many women in the benches began screaming at the governor to let her go. The lioness was turned into the arena, and, as it approached her, the women created a panic, clambering over the seats in an effort to reach the governor. The lioness, released from its cage, dashed across the arena until close to the unconscious victim, then slowly approached, as if getting ready to spring. Thekla had closed her eyes in terror; but the lioness, recognizing the body as that of her companion of the day before by the sense of smell, refused to attack her and tenderly licked Thekla's bare feet.

Alexander in great rage called for two bulls. Keepers drove the lioness to her cage. Guards brought the two bulls and hitched them by chains, one to the feet and the other to the head of the outstretched, unconscious Thekla, while other guards stood by with goads, to drive the bulls in opposite directions and pull her body in twain. The women had filled the section occupied by the governor and were shaking their clenched fists at him and screaming, "Murderer," "Brute," "Stop it."

Queen Tryphaena fainted. Because of the love they bore their native queen the men were aroused and joined in the demand that Thekla be released. The governor signed Alexander to release her, which he did reluctantly, in fear of the people. The shouts of joy aroused Tryphaena. Old as she was and with the dignity of queen, she eagerly hastened down to the arena. As she entered the arena she was stopped by a cry of pain close by her, for Aspasia had leaped to the arena from the wall, spraining her ankle. She was screaming from the pain and to attract Tryphaena. The queen turned aside and helped her to her feet. Aspasia insisted on limping along with the queen to Thekla. Reaching Thekla, the queen helped her to rise and enveloped her in her own regal cloak.

The queen and Aspasia led Thekla to the gates. When the gates were opened, there stood Thamyris, holding out his hands to Thekla.

"My shame has been before all the people," said Thekla.

"Come with me. I love you," said Thamyris.

"We have to tell the story of good news to the women of Asia," said Thekla, putting her arm around Aspasia. "You see that in the new freedom the two classes of women have met. We now understand each other through the power of love. I will go on my mission; if Aspasia wishes to turn back with you, she may."

"I, too, have found a love that is pure. We will go on and take the word to women of my class," said Aspasia.

"That man Paul has ruined our lives," Thamyris said, bitterly.

"Not Paul, except that he brought the truth to us, and we will take it to women who would be free in their souls," said Thekla. The three women, unconscious of the shouting multitude, went on their way, leaving Thamyris raging in his defeat.

CHAPTER XXXIII

"JOINT HEIRS"

It was in the early summer of 48 A.D. that Paul and Barnabas arrived at Lystra, 20 miles south of Iconium. They were smarting from the beatings they had received at Iconium. The people of the country spoke the native language of Lycaonia, and it was only in the cities of this land that the apostles could find people who understood the Greek language.

In Lystra Paul found a family with whom he made his home, Eunice, a Jewess, whose husband, a Greek, was dead. Her son Timothy, a lad fifteen years old, and her mother, Lois, constituted the family. The lad was very bright and Paul grew to love him; especially was he interesting to Paul, because Lois had taught him the Law and the Prophets, yet Timothy had never been subjected to the Jewish ordinances.

Paul's power to perform miracles was demonstrated in Lystra, when he healed a cripple. In the simplicity of their superstitions the people, led by the priests, were about to offer sacrifices to Paul and Barnabas, as gods. When the heralds refused to accept the high honors offered by the priests of the native cult, because it was idolatry, the priests immediately became offended at Paul. Jewish grain-buyers of Antioch, in the city at the time, urged how these men had been treated in Antioch and Iconium; and the priests led the people in an attack on Paul. They stoned him until he was unconscious; then, fearing what they had done, they dragged his body outside of the city. This occurred after the heralds had been there two months. Paul and Barnabas left for the border city of Derbe, 25 miles farther south. In the middle of the winter they started on a return to the cities through which they had passed. They went to the converts, who had been organized in bodies, and met with no public opposition. In Antioch Paul was again treated by Luke, the physician. They hastened on to the coast, so as to leave before the malarial period returned. Though once in a while, now many days apart, the attacks would come on Paul, yet he had recovered his strength in the high altitudes. On the way they stopped in Adada and held audiences in Perga.

In June, 49 A.D., the heralds took passage from Attaleia to Syrian Antioch.

Paul and Barnabas were occupied in Antioch, first in telling the wonderful results of their journey, and next in counteracting the activities of Judaists, who were spreading the doctrine that Gentiles accepting the gospel must comply with all Jewish requirements, even to the ceremonial washing before each meal, which was merely a sanitary symbol.

Paul would not yield one instant to the claims of the Judaizers who justified their course by saying they were just from James and the apostles in Jerusalem who had decided that Gentiles could not come into full fellowship under the gospel until they had complied with all the ordinances of Moses the same as Jesus himself had done. The argument had great weight with those leaders who were Jews and in the majority. Paul threw his supreme energy into this controversy; for hours at a time and for many days he confuted their arguments until baffled they persistently asserted their authority.

Paul fought for his cause, for the mighty purpose of Christ submitting to death on the cross that he might bring salvation to the world; he fought for converts from the Gentiles in whom he had planted some of the love of Jesus that actuated his own life. He was almost exhausted on the last day of the controversy, tears streamed down his cheeks as he plead that they would not insist on customs that would destroy the universal appeal of Jesus to men. His limbs trembled, his throat was parched, his voice was strained, emotion made him shake as with an ague, he reeled, he was falling. Friends leaped to aid him, but before they could reach him he recovered. A great calm came over him, he seemed to grow in stature and strength. He was silent—the hush settled over all—while with radiant face upturned he was listening as if he heard a voice. He looked upon the people with a smile of the generous victor and said in a sweet, impressive voice:

"It has been revealed to me that we should take this question before the elders in Jerusalem and have it settled once and forever."

Barnabas ably seconded the idea as the only sensible thing to do. The Judaists sought to be heard, but the elders and the congregation would not hear them, and immediately appointed Paul and Barnabas and others to go to Jerusalem to lay the question before the apostles and elders.

The Judaists left by boat, but Paul and Barnabas were so confident of the outcome that, taking Titus with them, they journeyed overland, stopping on the way to proclaim the glad tidings with the fervor and simplicity of their other journeys. Paul seemed more inspired than ever before and many Gentiles confessed Jesus as their Lord and Master. His companions had difficulty to persuade Paul to take time for rest and nourishment, for his zeal had been renewed or rather, if possible, he was inspired to greater efforts.

When Paul and Barnabas arrived in Jerusalem they found that the Judaists from Antioch having preceded them had secured the aid of some of the most learned who held their views to present their cause; and they had arranged for a large crowd of their friends to be present at the hearing. Paul convinced the apostles and elders that a public hearing would cause schisms and bitterness, and the hearing was before the small body of apostles and elders. Paul insisted on taking Titus in with him and Barnabas although it was well known that notwithstanding Titus had been active in relief of the suffering of Jerusalem and in missionary work he had never submitted to the Mosaic ordinances. The Judaists stated their cause as if the question had already been settled favorably to their contention and that they were only carrying out such interpretation.

When the time came for Paul to present his views he began without any reference to the controversy. He recalled his own conversion, the revelation to him, his years of work without so much as showing his face in Jerusalem, the appearance of Jesus to him, and that the things which had been revealed to him agreed with the understanding those who had walked with Jesus had from the Master. He told them of the power and influence of the glad tidings among the Gentiles wherever he and Barnabas had gone, and that these converts were spreading the teachings farther and faster than any other word had ever traveled, even to the remote corners of the world.

"Think you that this is all in vain?" he cried out, visibly holding his intense emotions in subjection so as to present the facts in orderly fashion. "Already the story of the cross has outrun the power of the law. Was the sacrifice of Jesus merely to extend burdensome customs which, he declared, by interpretation, killed inspiration? Or have I run in vain? Am I also deceiving myself? Would you withdraw the promise of the resurrection that Jesus made to all who would believe on him, and limit it only to Jews? He is the fulfilment of the law; and I am his servant to carry the glad tidings to all the world, first to the Jews and also to the Gentiles, for all who believe on him are joint heirs with him."

Then Peter rose and with his wonderful enthusiasm told of his vision in Joppa that led him to Cornelius, the centurion, who received the Holy Spirit, and that the way was opened for all Gentiles, saying:

"Now, therefore, why do you make trial of God, that you should put a yoke upon the neck of the disciples which neither your fathers nor we are able to bear?"

James, the leader of the apostles, answered that it seemed to him that they should not lay burdens on those that came from the Gentiles, only that they abstain from pollutions, from meats offered to idols and other commonly acknowledged wrongs. This met with approval, and it was embodied in a letter to the gentile converts at Antioch sent by special messengers, Judas and Silas,who returned with Paul and Barnabas to confirm the findings.

Apparently the Judaizers had been suppressed; and Paul rejoiced that the great stumbling-block of Judaism had been removed from the highway being thronged by Christian believers. Within a short time the Christians in Antioch felt that the vexing question of Judaism in the church had been settled and released Judas and Silas from any further duties to repeat and enforce the decision.

The Judaists did not accept the decision of the council in Jerusalem in the broad application which its terms indicated, but they set about to give a private interpretation among the Jews of the congregation that the decision only affected the rights of the Gentiles to become members and to be received in the public gatherings. The Judaizers persisted in their course until there was a withdrawal of social intercourse of many of the Jews with those of gentile origin, the separation being principally evidenced by the refusal of Jews to partake of meals in company with gentile members.

When Peter came up to Antioch during the late winter on his journey of inspection of the work, the Judaists appealed to him that their interpretation saved them to the seclusiveness of their own ritualism and saved them from becoming unclean under the Mosaic Law, while all the privileges of salvation were extended to the Gentiles. Without giving deep thought to the argument Peter was won to it and refused to sit at meat with the gentile members of the church lest he offend the conscience of the Jewish members. Even Barnabas was led into taking this view.

The Judaizers suddenly became open in their views, intending to take advantage of Peter's approval to carry their point. Until Peter had been won over to the side of the Judaizers they had kept their construction of the letter of the council from Paul.

Paul called a meeting of the elders as soon as the action of Peter and Barnabas came to his knowledge. He did not handle the subject delicately, nor did he permit the standing of Peter as an apostle to deter him. He accused him of eating with Gentiles until influential Judaists had raised this new question, and that now he insulted gentile brothers by refusing to sit at meat with them. "You vacillate," Paul charged Peter before the elders. "Before this question was raised you ate with Gentiles without becoming a Gentile, now, because these Judaizers make show of numbers, you would compel Gentiles to become Jews before they could eat with you. You are a dissembler, a play-actor. What confidence must we have in you? We are justified by faith in Jesus Christ, not by the works of the law. Speak the truth as you did at the council in Jerusalem."

Peter thought rapidly, and in his quickness to right a wrong humbly begged Paul to forget and forgive him this wrong, and then he told the assembly all that had taken place and that Paul was right. In like manner Barnabas retracted his action. From that day forth the Judaizers were powerless in Antioch, though they sought other fields, even in far Galatia.

In the spring of 50 A.D. Paul felt the urge to establish new organizations and to stabilize those already formed. Barnabas insisted on taking John Mark with them because he had repented of his former desertion and he was a competent attendant. The two old comrades could not agree on John Mark, so Barnabas took John Mark and sailed to Cyprus, and Paul selected Silas to go with him. Paul and Silas set out overland, visiting places Paul had gone to before he was called to Antioch. They came into Tarsus where Paul found a hearty welcome by his aged parents, and his old friends were now glad to discuss the glad tidings with him. Paul and Silas journeyed up through the Cilician gates, across the mountains and down through the cities Paul and Barnabas had visited.

Stopping at Lystra with his old friends, Eunice and Lois, Paul found that Timothy had rapidly grown to manhood and had been well schooled in the Scriptures, and had been thoroughly grounded in the glad tidings according to the things which the apostle had taught them on his former visits.

The proposed trip either to the Far East or northeast appealed to Timothy. He begged to join Paul and Silas, and he argued that his own horse would be sufficient for him. Paul listened to the plea and persuaded Eunice to let her boy go with them. In evidence of his regard for the Jewish customs and to convince Eunice that her own religion would be a safeguard for her son, Paul circumcised Timothy. Thus it was that the young man, Timothy, entered into the life of Paul.

The three travelers set forth from Lystra, uncertain of their destination. In Antioch of Pisidia Paul again met Luke, to whom he rehearsed the controversy about the call to the Gentiles. This so encouraged Luke that he volunteered to join the party. They went forth along the mountain roads to the east and north. Looking down the rivers flowing to the east and north, Paul felt that not any good was to be accomplished in those regions which looked forbidding from the mountains.

They found no suitable places to stop and, after many days of travel, they reached Troas. Luke had been telling Paul of the great needs in Macedonia.

That night Paul had a vision of Luke standing by and begging him to come over into Macedonia. When Paul told his companions of the dream, they agreed that it was a confirmation of the suggestion to go to Macedonia. That very day they set sail and, reaching Neapolis, they journeyed to Philippi, in which city there were many Romans.

Paul and his companions had been traveling from June until August. While resting for a few days they became acquainted with the customs of the people. Women without veils went about the streets; men affected more generally the Roman dress; there were so few Jews that there was no synagogue. Jews who worshiped went to a spot selected on the river, and were often accompanied by the "God-fearers." In this land women had greater privileges than in Asia. Among the "God-fearers" was an influential tradeswoman by the name of Lydia, a dealer in the purple cloth from Thyatira, highly prized in Philippi. Paul met her at the place of worship by the riverside and she was won by his earnest presentation of the glad tidings. She accepted the teachings and lavished on Paul every attention, extending to him the hospitality of her commodious home, both for himself and his companions, as well as a place of meeting.

An insane, afflicted girl, who, in her half-witted manner, told fortunes for the fees paid her Jewish owners, followed Paul, crying out:

"These men are servants of the Most High God."

After some days Paul became weary of her irresponsible outcry and, turning to her, he commanded the evil spirit to come out of her. Immediately she was restored to her right mind; and her owners, in rage, seizing Paul and Silas, took them before the magistrate and cunningly charged them with stirring up sedition against Rome. The rabble followed, demanding the punishment of Paul and Silas. The heralds knew that it was useless to demand justice there. Contrary to law, the magistrates ordered them flogged without trial. Then, bruised and bleeding, they were thrown into jail. They could not sleep and were singing, when an earthquake rocked the jail. The chains holding the prisoners dropped from the broken walls; the doors flew open; the jailer, with a light, rushed in. Seeing the doors open, he was sure that his prisoners had escaped; and, knowing the disgrace of allowing prisoners to escape, he was about to fall on his sword when Paul called out to him:

"Do yourself no harm, for we are all here."

The jailer listened to the wonderful story Paul told of Jesus of Nazareth, and believed. The magistrates in their superstition thought that the earthquake was because they had accused, flogged, and thrown Paul and Silas in jail without trial; and they sent word to the jailer in the morning to release the prisoners.

"They have beaten us, uncondemned Romans, cast us in jail, and do they now cast us out privily?" said Paul, when the jailer reported the directions of the magistrates. "Let them come themselves and bring us out."

The magistrates were so scared that they hastened to beg Paul and Silas to come out and to leave, lest the rabble would attack them. Paul and Silas went to the home of Lydia; and, bidding her farewell, they went on their way to Thessalonica, where they tarried until May, 51 A.D. At that time the Jews led the rabble against the Christians and took one Jason, whom they compelled to give security for Paul and Silas to keep the peace, upon the charge that they were teaching that one Jesus was king, instead of Caesar.

Paul and Silas were sent away to Beroea, where they met with great success and kindly treatment, until the Jews of Thessalonica appeared and stirred up the people. Paul had been very successful in gaining as converts honorable Greek women. After a conference, it was decided to send him to Athens, where he waited for Timothy and Silas.

CHAPTER XXXIV

ATHENS AND CORINTH

During the days of waiting for Silas and Timothy, Paul indulged a craving, renewed from his days in Nestor's school, to see the sculpture, paintings, and architecture of Athens. In his soul was a longing for the expression of the beautiful. He spent days on the Acropolis and in the temples, reveling in the sculptured and pictured masterpieces of the geniuses of ancient Greece. The portrayals of the human form did not appeal to nor excite the carnal eye—they were spiritual revelations. Again and again he contemplated the Parthenon, growing more beautiful the more closely it was scrutinized; the wonderful art shown in its columns, proportions, and simplicity was exalting. In the Parthenon the gold and ivory statue of Athena, 36 feet high, on a pedestal 8 feet high, was not a vulgar sex-goddess, but it typified dignity, power, and beauty.

Paul felt that the highest art was only an effort to express the longings of the spiritually minded for perfection; and that Jesus was an expression of divinity in human form, unequaled by artists. He believed that the great masters had produced their marvels by rising above all grossness; and he was thrilled with the thought that his mission was to stir all men to emulate this purity and beauty of love, as found in the life of the Master.

Paul found that the fawning Athenians had chiseled the names of Roman generals and officers on many of the masterpieces of artists of bygone centuries, as fulsome compliments to Roman vanity. Even, in some cases, the heads had been removed from splendid statues and replaced, in grotesque contrast with the beauty of the body, by the chiseled features of Roman officers to whom the doubtful honor was given. Paul was grieved to learn that the frivolous Athenians made no serious protest against such vandalism, merely laughing at the egotism of the Romans. The elements had not destroyed, during the long centuries, the delicate touch of genius in marble, but Athenian indifference to the rich heritage had cruelly permitted the works of inspiration to be battered and bartered for the favor of coarse conquerors.

The beautiful stoas, or porches, surrounding the Agora, or Market Place, afforded loungers ideal accommodations. In the Poecile Stoa, or Painted Porch, containing the paintings of Polygnotus, where once had gathered the scholars who evolved the Stoic philosophy, now loitered the idling, incessantly talking rhetoricians and teachers, pleased merely to debate any new question. The discovery of philosophy by earnest men of leisure in the past was now a precedent for profitless discussions, as an excuse for idleness. They did not have the virility of their gifted ancestors, who had made war in order to supply themselves with wealth and slaves so that they could have leisure for the study of politics, philosophy, and art.

These loiterers preferred soft shades to the toil and thrill of adventure. They had exchanged the spirituality of their race for the love of idleness. Their learning exhausted itself in the application of the rules of speech and of logic to the presentation of any fact or theory, without seriously considering the substance—it was the decadent period of Greece. Even the ancient blonde type was being supplanted by those of darker complexion, who pretended that they inherited Grecian pride. The altar Paul had seen on the Acropolis, dedicated, in the uncertainty of doubt, to "The Unknown God," epitomized the Greek mind of that day.

Paul often joined in the conversations of the different groups of politicians and scholars, lounging in the porches about the Market Place, in an effort to direct the discussion to immortality. Some had called him a mountebank of philosophy, others said he was merely a picker-up of crumbs of thought. After a few days of discussions with groups, a number of leading men insisted that Paul should meet them the next day in the Areopagus, the place of large gatherings.

Before the large assembly Paul began his address by appealing to the religious ideas of the Athenians, although he knew that they did not have any settled religious beliefs. He declared to them that all men should seek God, although he was not far from each man, and then he quoted a line from Aratus, which he had learned in Nestor's school:

His offspring are we.

He asserted that the appearance of Jesus among men was a revelation of God, and assured them that through him came the resurrection of the dead. At this the Athenians laughed, for they could not even understand that Plato meant anything like resurrection when he discussed the immortality of the soul. They listened with critical ears to test Paul's message by their rules of logic, and had no ears for a message that would regulate their lives. Paul's appeal fell on unhearing ears; to them he was only a babbler. Dionysius, a member of the court, was led to believe; and a poor woman by the name of Damaris was informed by Paul that her faith gave her the assurances of the promises. The indifference and ridicule of the Athenians so disgusted Paul that he left for Corinth.

Paul noticed, on entering Corinth, a massive monument in the form of a lion, holding under its paw a lamb, with an inscription dedicating it to Lais, the most noted courtesan of the city. The Market Place was surrounded with temples and porches that rivaled the art of Athens. A broad roadway led up the Acrocorinthus, a thousand feet above, on which was the famous temple erected to Aphrodite, in which were more than a thousand courtesans, or hetairai, who openly solicited men in the Market Place and gave their earnings to sustain the temple. The restoration of the city by Julius Caesar, after its destruction a century before his time, had made Corinth the emporium of Greece. Many cargoes were transported across the isthmus, and even small boats were taken across on rollers from Lechaeum, on the Corinthian Gulf, and relaunched at Schoenus, thus avoiding the long and dangerous journey around the peninsula.

The reputation of the city was such that the slang of the period summed up excessive debauchery in the word, "Corinthianize." While the Greeks were in the majority, they submitted to the domination of the Roman colonists; and the Jews, attracted by the commercial advantages, made no protest against the customs.

So degenerate had the city become that even the families of Corinth were frequently lax in the morals which were necessary for any degree of citizenship, even to the extent that women who were married were expected, as a religious offering, to make or to have made a contribution to the support of the temple from their earnings of at least one sacrificial act of prostitution.

Paul knew all this about Corinth and much more rarely written. With his quick judgment he decided that in this city of great activity and recklessness many men and women would be found glad of an opportunity to enable them to rise superior to their sordid surroundings. In his effort to adapt his argument at Athens to the philosophical style he felt not only that he had failed to present unequivocally Christ as the great fact of spiritual life but that he had fallen short of his unswerving loyalty to Jesus. He resolved that henceforth he would present the loving and sacrificial life of Jesus in all its simplicity and grandeur as the supreme sacrifice of the Creator for the creature; neither controversy, dogmas, nor systems of philosophy would be able to drive or lure him from presenting the divine heroism of Christ as the great revelation of the love of God.

Paul had given his life to make plain to men the marvelous power of his hero, Jesus Christ, his Lord and Master. He believed that men would understand from this message the love and sacrifice of Christ, and that from such understanding would come a knowledge of all the virtues for all ages and the certainty of the resurrection to those to whom it was promised.

Paul, leaving Athens behind him, entered Corinth determined "not to know anything save Jesus Christ,

and him crucified." While wandering among the shops
and booths he met a tent-maker by the name of Aquila,
who, with his wife, Priscilla, had been driven out of
Rome under an edict of Claudius against the Jews.
Paul introduced himself, and was pleased to find that
the couple had been followers of the Way in Rome and
had heard of his work. He immediately set to work
with them at his trade and, while his malaria returned
because of the climate, he began teaching in the synagogue. His friends, Silas and Timothy, soon joined
him; and they brought such news of errors into which
the converts were falling that he was compelled to write
a long letter to the Thessalonians. He received contributions from the faithful brothers in Philippi and, notwithstanding murmurings of the Jews, he applied himself
more zealously than ever to his work.

Aquila and Priscilla told him of the teachings in
Rome and that people from the northland came there
and heard the tidings, from the far west in Spain, even
from a land far away beyond the mountains, forests,
and rivers and across a sea to the north, called
Britain. During this time the news came to Paul about
troubles stirred up by Judaists in the churches he had
established in Galatia. He wrote a letter to the Galatians, which was carefully read over by others before
it was sent. Visitors from Rome, calling on Aquila
and Priscilla, became acquainted with Paul, telling
him about the difficulties of keeping the word clear
in Rome.

"Why do you not write a letter to our Roman
brethren?" said Aquila. "They need to understand
things more clearly."

"I would," Paul replied, "only I have never talked to them, save those I have met here."

"Write them along the lines of your letter to the Galatians," said Aquila, "but more in detail. The world meets in Rome."

"I hope for the day that I may meet those in Rome," said Paul. "It seems to me that the great city would be the best center from which to spread the glad tidings through the length and breadth of the Roman Empire."

"The day may come," Priscilla said.

"I so long for it that I fear I may anticipate the proper time," said Paul. "Those I have met here are deeply interested."

The Jews having raised an outcry against Paul teaching in the synagogue, he quit them in anger and, by the gesture of shaking out his robe as if shaking crumbs out of his lap, he gave them distinctly to understand that he was through with the Jews of Corinth who would not listen to the new teaching.

When the Jews saw that Paul was determined to carry on his work in the house of Titus Justus, they laid complaint before Gallio, the new proconsul, who had, a month or two before (July, 52 A.D.), come to rule over Achaia, that Paul was persuading men to worship God contrary to the law. A coppersmith by the name of Alexander was active in stirring up the Jews to make the complaint before the new proconsul.

Sosthenes, the ruler of the synagogue, appeared at the head of a delegation before Gallio, at the time of the trial. The loiterers from the porches and Market Place filled the hall of hearing, for it was great sport to them to see the despised Jews in trouble. Paul was brought before Gallio, who, making excuse to identify the prisoner, had him brought closer, when he saw a faint scar across Paul's left temple. After the Jews had made their complaint, Gallio laughed heartily. Paul was about to make his defense.

"If these are questions about words, names, and your own law, look to it yourselves, you Jews," said Gallio. "I am not minded to waste my time on these things. Lictors, drive them out. They know better than to impose on me this way."

Then, turning to Paul, Gallio smiled and said, "We will play the game according to the rules."

Gallio engaged Paul in conversation concerning their old days in the school of Nestor in Tarsus, smiling indifferently while the rabble, in rough humor, relieved the lictors of their duty by seizing Sosthenes and beating him, while he ran out of the hall.

During his stay of eighteen months in Corinth, Paul had established a large and substantial organization, and in the spring of 53 A.D. started for Syria, accompanied by Aquila and Priscilla. But he was taken ill at the seaport of Cenchreae, where he was delayed for some time and tenderly nursed by Phoebe. There he cut his hair in token of a vow, and carried it with him to be burned in the Temple when he would reach Jerusalem, agreeable to a Jewish custom.

Touching at Ephesus for a short stay, he left Aquila and Priscilla there, while he hastened on to Jerusalem and then back to Antioch. From there he made a hasty trip through Galatia and Phrygia, arriving in Ephesus in the fall of the year.

CHAPTER XXXV

EPHESUS

During the three months that Paul taught in the synagogue in Ephesus, a Jew a little older than Paul, the same Alexander who had been active in Corinth, a regular attendant, interrupted the discourses frequently with many questions; and he stirred up other Jews in opposition to Paul. Alexander delighted, mockingly, in taking a prominent place among those in the front part of the audience; and, by grimaces of disagreement, cynical laughter, and conversation with others, he sought to disconcert Paul, often succeeding. He fomented such opposition that finally the Jews drove Paul out of the synagogue.

So successful had been his work in Ephesus, attracting influential men of the city and from near by and even distant cities of Asia, that Paul and his friends hired a hall used by Tyrannus, a teacher; but they were compelled to use it after the morning classes. Paul worked at his trade from early morning light until eleven o'clock, and then spent the rest of the day teaching. He won prominent men and attracted great crowds of common people. The superstitious people carried away handkerchiefs and small articles that he had touched, for talismen to restore the sick. He declaimed against all superstition so effectively that the people, who, having been long used to all forms of necromancy and having spent much of their wealth for charms and books on magic, brought their books and charms together and made a monster bonfire, destroying books valued at ten thousand dollars (fifty thousand drachmae). It was the breaking of the superstition of ages.

Alexander even followed Paul to the meetings in the hall and often interrupted the discourse. Whenever Paul referred to his experience on the way to Damascus, Alexander would cry out:

"Did you ever repay the cost of your trip to Caiaphas?"

"That I did," Paul finally answered, "with earnings of my own hands, while I was in Arabia. Now tell us who bears your expense to follow me from Corinth?"

This created such commotion, by efforts to put Alexander out (which he did not seriously resist) and the shouting of men brought in by him, that the meeting was dismissed. He continued actively in stirring up all opposition to the apostle. In the face of all efforts to discourage him, Paul made great progress during his two years in Ephesus.

Ephesus was the center of trade for Asia; close to the mouth of the river Caystros, with extensive docks; the western end of trade routes to the Euphrates; famous in literature and art; renowned for native philosophers, astronomers, poets, and painters—but Ephesus achieved its greatest fame by its wonderful temple, erected to "the Great Goddess Artemis," one of the Seven Wonders of the World. The temple was finished in polished marble and its porches had one hundred and twenty-seven columns, 60 feet in height. It was 425 feet in length and 220 feet in width, and contained the image of the goddess Artemis, studded with breasts symbolizing fecundity.

The temple had been two hundred and twenty years in the building; the vast expense had been borne by the contributions of all the people of Asia, even the women giving their jewels and ornaments. The temple and a large area surrounding it was so sacred that it was an asylum for anyone fleeing from officers. The multitudes, gathering during the month of feasts, by their purchases added to the wealth of the city, and increased the trade in miniature productions of the goddess and temple, in gold, silver, brass, and pottery. Ephesus was called "the Light of Asia."

The influence of the great numbers who had joined the Way was so strong against the worship of idols that the sale of miniatures fell off, to the detriment of dealers. Alexander, being a coppersmith, pointed out to his friend, Demetrius, a silversmith, that Paul and his associates had so spread his preaching against idols that the business of the dealers in images was being permanently injured.

"If you, because of your high standing, would explain the conditions to the craftsmen," said Alexander to Demetrius, "what Paul is doing, and make the plea as if in behalf of Artemis, you could arouse the people so that they would drive him out of Ephesus."

"I am not such an orator as is Paul and I fear that I could not move the people," Demetrius answered, doubtfully.

"Make the appeal for your goddess and you will arouse the century-old prejudice," Alexander urged. "I know, for I do not believe in her, but as a Jew I am advising you, so that you can win your point. I am in agreement with you to drive out Paul. When you have aroused your people, I will make an appeal that will cause the Jews to join you."

Demetrius called his fellow-craftsmen together and explained the injury being done to the trade and the attack Paul and his kind were making on the temple and worship of Artemis. Fired with religious fervor and mercenary motives, the craftsmen poured into the streets shouting many things, and soon had attracted a great mob. They seized Gaius and Aristarchus, Paul's companions, and carried them to the great open-air theater of the city. In the midst of the wild acclaim, "Great Artemis of the Ephesians," the Jews lifted Alexander to the stage to explain the attitude of the Jews, as merchants and dealers, and to tell the mob that the Jews would join in driving Paul out of the city.

A Jew was no more popular with the mob than was Paul, for he was a Jew. Alexander, from his elevation, posed as one with an important and friendly message. The mob, now beside itself with much shouting, screamed:

"He, too, is a Jew. A Jew! A Jew! Great Artemis of the Ephesians!"

They pulled him down from the stage, they cuffed him about and tore his clothes and pulled at his beard, until his friends rescued him, in most unhappy state.

Paul wanted to go before the crowd and meet them. Not only his own friends of the Way opposed such course, but the Asiarchs, the officers in charge of festivals, who were friendly to Paul, also dissuaded him.

Paul had been training men for two years, from Smyrna, Pergamos, Thyatira, Sardes, Philadelphia, Colossae, and Laodicea, to carry the glad tidings and to organize the believers in self-governing bodies through-out the province. He was convinced that Rome was now his destination, since the work in Asia had been so established that it would go forward without his personal attention. He had learned the effectiveness of his letters, which not only settled the immediate controversies but would serve for future guidance in keeping the faith to simple and fundamental principles. The conditions in Corinth required many letters and special messengers.

Taking with him a few reliable men, including Timothy and Trophimus, Paul set out for a visitation of the converts throughout Macedonia and Greece, in the course of which he would attach Luke to his company at Philippi.

"I am determined to go to Corinth," said Alexander to Demetrius, "to be ahead of Paul and his company, who are going there through Macedonia."

"Of what avail will be such a journey?" Demetrius asked.

"If you and your friends will finance my trip," said Alexander, "I will follow Paul until he is put out of the way; and if he is removed, then all these teachings and his followers will fail."

"What would it profit you?" Demetrius asked. "Why are you so vindictive against him?"

"I am a Jew and my opinions are fixed," said Alexander. "Many years ago, in Jerusalem, this same Jesus about whom Paul preaches was on his way to his Crucifixion and dared me to oppose him. I laughed at him, aye, I spat upon him. I knew this Paul, then Saul, when as a zealot he was persecuting the people of the Way. He turned traitor and has become so powerful that my life is dedicated to getting rid of him, so that he will not be a martyr in the eyes of the converts. You cannot understand the satisfaction it would give me to accomplish my desires. That is something which would be of greater value to me than riches; it would be revenge on the man who, streaming with sweat, turned on me in assumed saintliness and pronounced a curse, that I should await his return; and neighbors laughed at me so that I had to change my name and business. I could get my revenge and you business profit by destroying this religion. Without Paul it will fail."

"I never hope to understand a Jew," said Demetrius, "but I will furnish you the money for this undertaking."

CHAPTER XXXVI

PLOTS THAT FAILED

Paul, with his companions, left Ephesus in January, 56 A.D., and spent the time, until early summer, in Troas, diligently applying himself to teaching and writing. His fifty-five years of active life and his later years of hardship and anxieties were beginning to show in his age. Though a sufferer from malaria, often renewed by passing through the lands in which it was prevalent, he did not slacken in energy. The advancing years made him more anxious to speed up his work and to cover the lands still needing the uplift of the glad tidings. He crossed over into Macedonia in the early summer, and spent the fall and winter in visiting over the ground he had years before traveled.

His added mission now was to carry over into the Way the practical ideas of brotherhood and relief that he had learned as a rabbi, which ideas he conceived were the very essence of brotherly love. He urged, wherever he went, that all should contribute to a fund to sustain the poor and persecuted brothers in Jerusalem. He drove home the thought that practical morality should be enforced; that mere belief in Jesus gave no promise, unless the spirituality of his life was expressed in daily life; that love was not an abstract term, but a command to do the things that relieved the distress of others. He gave to his appreciation of Jesus an application in the corrupt life of the age that would save not only the souls of believers but would save civilization.

While he did not hold forth as a reformer of civil laws, he planted the idea of freedom of conscience in the mind of the slave and of love in the heart of the master, so that justice was recognized and equality of mind was demonstrated, trusting that in the fulness of time men would come to understand the life of Jesus and to imitate the freedom of the soul in civil righteousness.

With his company changing from time to time, by reason of the missions delegated to different ones, Paul arrived in Corinth in the winter and tarried there until March of 57 A.D. He was almost selfish in his desire to have Timothy with him, for his great heart yearned for the love of his own son and Timothy occupied the place of the son who had passed on.

In Corinth he found an improvement in conditions among the converts of the Way, although it had been a long, hard struggle for him, Timothy, his most trusted teachers, the eloquent Apollos, and Peter, to hold them to a life devoted to higher ideals than permitted by Corinthian environments. His appeals for funds for the relief of the brothers in Jerusalem were being splendidly answered. The members in Corinth resolutely set themselves against the degradation of the city, which was becoming more attractive to the patricians of Rome in the rapidly degenerating morality of the capital of the Empire. The news which he had from Rome aroused his growing desire to visit the city, not only to spread the word throughout the world but to establish the pure morals of the Way and to take hope to the slaves, who were nearly one-half of the city's population.

It was during this stay in Corinth, at the home of Gaius, that Paul wrote his remarkable Letter to the Romans. He had with him for consultation Timothy, Luke, and Sopater, while Tertius took the dictation. He intended to make plain the breadth and the depth of the love exemplified in the life of Jesus and in his promises. The unseemly display of the hetairai in the Market Place, the brazen temple of Aphrodite on the mountain top, with its nameless orgies, aroused Paul to appeal to the knowledge of God that all men had in times past received, whether Jew or Gentile. In sharp contrast with the present-day licentiousness, he gave them the Beatitudes of the soul of the believer in Jesus. He reminded them of the faith that gave men the power to believe, to live up to the purity and become partakers of the love revealed by Christ, and to be justified by their faith in him, so that they would receive freedom from fear on earth and the assurance of the resurrection.

From the house of Gaius, Paul's host, Paul, Gaius, Luke, Timothy, Trophimus, and several others were on their way to the place of meeting of the congregation. While passing through a long, beautiful porch, they stopped in the earnest discussion of plans. They noticed a group of loungers near the front of the porch and had stopped so that their conversation would not be overheard. They did not see that one of the loungers had given a signal to a group of hetairai, parading along the front of the stoas or porches; but, shortly, twenty of the girls from the temple, in their filmy and scant clothing, with cymbals and trumpets, crowded down the porch and tauntingly jostled Paul and his friends.

The loungers laughed loudly. After the girls had passed on Paul and his friends went to the Market Place, where they paused for a moment to separate, some going on errands and others with Paul going to the place of meeting. Paul looked closely at the group of loungers and recognized Alexander, in deep conversation with the rest.

"Hasten," said Alexander to a bearded Greek, after Paul had passed, "and have the hetairai come back into the Market Place and surround Paul and his deacons."

The parading women, augmented by another group they had met, came into the Market Place through another porch, so that they intercepted Paul on his way to the hall. There were many men, ogling at the side of the line of girls. The leader of the girls in the parade, on seeing Paul, stopped her followers and said:

"Ho, you charmers of Aphrodite. Here is our enemy, Paul. We will make sport of him. Follow me."

She led her followers in mocking honor around Paul, in a voluptuous dance. She stopped in front of him in suggestive contortions, laughing and shouting. Alexander and his loungers came closer, joining in the laughter. Paul looked upon the dancer with such earnestness that she stopped dancing and, in a surge of shame, hung her head.

"Even as you refuse to have God in your knowledge," said Paul impressively to the girl before him, "he gives you up unto a reprobate mind, to do those things which are not decent."

The leader of the parade turned in shame and left, followed by the other women. Alexander, being close to Paul, sneered at him. The men with Alexander were laughing loudly. Paul looked Alexander in the eye fearlessly and wrathfully and said:

"Remember, you who judge them that practice such things, and do the same, that you shall not escape the judgment of God."

Alexander was unable to meet the charge or the gaze of Paul.

Paul and his friends went on their way to the hall used for meeting, and Alexander shortly followed them to listen. Paul was telling all in the hall that the contributions had been liberal, that the money must be safeguarded, and that the company going to Jerusalem must set sail from Cenchreae on the first ship. One of the men inside the hall, suspecting that there was an eavesdropper, opened the door quickly, disclosing Alexander, who slouched back to his associates in the porch.

When Alexander returned to the porch, the bearded Greek was railing against Paul.

"And even the women of my own house have turned against me, refusing to earn money by taking guests, because they are followers of the Way, and they say that would be a sin against their souls." The Greek had to stop speaking because of his laughter. Then he said, "As if women could have souls."

While the Greek was speaking, a dandified Greek youth in fine raiment, carrying a string of beads which he drew through his fingers for amusement, entered the porch.

"I hear that Nero is about to establish a voice-culture school in Corinth, as soon as he collects the taxes for it," said the youth, flippantly.

The men merely glanced at the youth disdainfully.
He reclined on a bench near by, and, taking out of his
girdle some pipes, began playing softly, as if the men were
not present and as if their conversation had no interest
for him.

"Paul goes with a large sum of money," said Alexander to the Greek, "on the next ship sailing toward
Jerusalem."

"No doubt my family have contributed," said the
Greek in anger.

"If a man would slip aboard the ship," said Alexander,
while the youth struggled apparently to get the right
note, "he could not only get that money but in that
crowd he might heave the body overboard, undiscovered,
and that would be bad."

"This is my opportunity," said the Greek, "You,
as a Jew, can be going to Jerusalem, and I will be going
to Troas."

The youth arose, stretched himself, put his pipes
in his girdle, took out his string of beads, thoughtlessly
playing with them, and sauntered to the front of the
porch. After looking up and down the Market Place,
as if uncertain which way to go, he passed down to the
hall where Paul and his friends were in conference. He
burst in very excitedly. His assumed light air was
gone, for he was known and trusted as one who believed
in the Way. He told of the plot.

"Alexander has followed me for years," said Paul.
"I have often thought that I saw him at the stoning of
Stephen, although he is no older now than he was then.
I am sure he led the mob against us here in Corinth five

years ago. I know that he was at Ephesus, but there
he became the victim of his own schemes. It is no
matter. Dangers have always beset me."

"I advise that you slip away from the others at
Cenchreae," said Luke, "and make them think that
you have boarded the ship. Our friends will go by ship
to Troas and we will go to Neapolis; from there we will
take ship to meet them in Troas."

When news came that a ship was sailing for Troas,
Paul and his friends went to Cenchreae the night before,
stopping with friends, to board the ship in the early
morning. The passengers were crowding aboard in the
dark of the early morning. Paul had been wearing a
peculiarly marked cloak of broad stripes. While waiting
their turn to go aboard, the friends of Paul noticed
Alexander and the bearded Greek scanning the passengers. Trophimus and Paul exchanged cloaks, and, by
turning up the broad collar, Trophimus concealed his
shaven face. Alexander and the Greek, recognizing the
cloak of Paul in the dim light, followed Trophimus
aboard, while Paul and Luke returned and made their
trip overland to Neapolis.

After the early morning breeze had carried the ship
out on its course, the Greek and Alexander set about to
locate Paul among the passengers. The small ship was
crowded to capacity with Jews, who were on their way
to celebrate the Passover in Jerusalem, and almost every
available place was occupied. In the forward part of the
ship they saw Trophimus, wearing Paul's cloak, with his
back toward them. He was on the farther side of a pile
of luggage nearly as high as his waist and no one appeared

in view near him.   Most of the passengers were taking
a nap, to make up for the loss of sleep in boarding the
ship early in the morning.

The Greek and Alexander made their way unobtru-
sively toward Trophimus, whom they identified as Paul
by the cloak.   The Greek carried a heavy club concealed;
Alexander followed closely, keeping a sharp lookout
for any who might be observing.   The Greek stepped
around the higher part of the bundles and with drawn
club was advancing to strike Trophimus, when Aristarchus, lying concealed behind the bundles, grasped him
by the ankle and threw him on his face.   Aristarchus and
others had concealed themselves behind the bundles to
guard Trophimus, taking turns in resting.   Alexander
immediately interceded to prevent any outcry.   .

"Do not be angry or frightened," said Alexander to
Trophimus, who had faced the Greek, now rising.
"This man is a countryman of yours, and had I not
seen him stumble, I, too, would have thought that he was
going to strike you."

"I certainly had no desire to strike you," said the
Greek.

"We understand you very well," said Trophimus.

When the Greek and Alexander were to themselves
the Greek said:

"I am through.   We have been badly fooled."

"Paul is so cunning that I know he cannot be honest,"
said Alexander.   "But I will follow him; a few months,
even years, are nothing to me."

The ship having reached Troas many days before
Paul and Luke, the followers of the Way set about to
have a great conference when Paul would arrive.   They

hired an assembly-room on the third floor, and in other
parts of the building they lodged and fed the visitors
who were brought in from the country and the smaller
towns to participate. Meanwhile, Paul was delayed
and observed the Passover in Philippi, which in that
year (57 A.D.) began April 6 and continued until the
evening of April 14. He and Luke were four days in
crossing over to Troas.

Paul's friends in Troas kept daily watch for his
arrival, so that he would not be alone even from the
landing to the place of lodging. They had seen Alexander in conference with many questionable men and
with those Jews who were opposed to the movement.

CHAPTER XXXVII

FELIX TREMBLES

Paul and Luke arrived at Troas April 19, 57 A.D., and, by the time their boat reached the landing, a large crowd of their friends gathered to greet them. At the same time, Alexander assembled several Jews who had not accepted the new doctrine, and was haranguing them to convince them that Paul's work all over the world was destroying the religion of Moses.

"He is the only one able to make the new religion universal," said Alexander. "If we get rid of him, we are forever free of these apostate disturbers. So many of them are gathered here that we could start a disturbance; and in it this Greek, who came with me, might find a chance to satisfy himself and to remove Paul."

"We are not concerned with your plans," said a leader of the orthodox Jews. "Troas has had a bad name for brawls, but we are not going to be caught in anything unlawful. The soldiers are very strict; and besides, these people, some of them as good Jews as we are, do not molest us, and we will leave them alone."

Alexander was not deterred from his purpose, although the Greek sailed on the vessel that had brought Paul and Luke. Alexander watched Paul for the seven days that he was in Troas, but the disciples hovered about the apostle so that no stranger could get near him.

The last night Paul was in Troas, a young man by the name of Eutychus, having gone to sleep in the window of the room on the third floor, where Paul was speaking, fell to the street below. Even Luke, the physician, thought the youth was dead, but Paul took the body in his arms and declared his life was still in him. There was great rejoicing when the young man soon recovered. All night long Paul talked with his friends, and, at break of day, he set out on foot, going to Assos, a distance of 20 miles, where he met his companions, who had come in a hired boat. Alexander was compelled to wait many days before he could gain a passage to Syria.

Paul and his company sailed to Mitylene and in four days' sailing they came to Miletus, where he met the elders, who came down from Ephesus. He had a premonition that he would never see them again and his address to them was a solemn farewell. They sailed to Cos, thence to Rhodes, and on to Patara, where they took passage on another ship to Tyre. While the ship tarried seven days in Tyre, unloading, Paul visited with the disciples, who so loved him that they came down to the beach with their families, and lingeringly bade him farewell. Sailing to Ptolemais, Paul and his companions stopped with the friends in that city, and then came the next day to Caesarea, where they lodged with Philip, the evangelist.

The four daughters of Philip were teachers, with whose work Paul was so delighted that he prolonged his visit. Timothy and Trophimus went to the Roman office and registered the party, according to the custom, for a journey to Jerusalem; and then engaged horses to carry them on their way. While engaging their horses, they saw Alexander, who had just arrived, and they were filled with fear that he would contrive some harm to Paul.

Agabus, the prophet, who had years before foretold at Antioch the famine in Jerusalem, had come down from Jerusalem; and, meeting Paul in the house of Philip, he dramatically prophesied that Paul would be bound as a prisoner in Jerusalem. Agabus wound Paul's girdle about his own feet and said:

"So shall the Jews at Jerusalem bind the man that owns this girdle, and shall deliver him into the hands of the Gentiles."

All present, with great sorrow and love, urged Paul not to go to Jerusalem.

"What do you," said Paul, "weeping and breaking my heart? I am ready not to be bound only, but also to die at Jerusalem."

On the journey to Jerusalem Paul reminiscently recalled his first journey over the same road, when, as a lad, his father was taking him to the school of Gamaliel. Often he had fretted at the austerity and unwavering convictions of his father, but now he remembered the love and pride of that strong man. He was devoutly thankful that so much of experience and love had come into his own life. Sympathy had displaced hate; love had supplanted pride; tolerance had driven out sectarianism; devotion to the elevation of humanity supplied him with unfaltering zeal; and his love for Jesus had made him a sacrificing messenger.

The first view of the Holy City thrilled him once again, but with new emotions, for it was the center of the new force in the world; the city over which his Master had wept, because of the love he had for it; the place of the Crucifixion and of the Resurrection, which gave hope to the world. The narrowness characterizing the Jews and the disciples was offset by the glory of the message that he had been commissioned to proclaim to the world.

Paul and his companions were welcomed by James and the elders and they rejoiced in all that the glad tidings had achieved—they lived in Jerusalem.

"Thousands of Jews, zealous for the law, have accepted our faith," said James to Paul. "However, they hear that you teach the Jews among the Gentiles to forsake the Law of Moses and to cease circumcision. They will hear that you have come."

"I have never ceased to be a Jew, nor have I ever advised any Jew to refrain from obedience to the law. I do not insist that Gentiles shall become Jews before they become Christians. Even now I am under a vow, to be fulfilled in the Temple, as a strict Jew," said Paul with warmth.

"We have no doubt of you," replied James. "As a matter of policy, to set at naught all complaints, take with you into the Temple four men we have here under vows, paying their charges, and that will be the final answer to your critics."

"I will do it," said Paul, "for it in no manner violates my conscience, although it is an indirect way of telling the truth."

The next day Paul and his companions, including Trophimus, were passing along the street, when Alexander, in conference with a priest and three others, pointed out Paul, saying:

"I have followed him from Corinth. He preaches against the Law of Moses, yet he is on his way to the Temple with that Greek, by the name of Trophimus.

Note them well, and no doubt he will take the Greek into the Temple."

Alexander was so interested in talking that he did not notice that he and his friends were blocking the narrow street; and, turning to leave, he jostled against James, who was walking with Timothy.

"You are one of the gabblers of the Way," said Alexander insolently to James.

"And, save you do not show the lapse of years," said James, with dignity, "I would say that you are that Ahasuerus, the shoemaker, who spat on Jesus while he was bearing his cross to Calvary."

"Not so; no, no," protested Alexander in fright. "I am Alexander, the coppersmith, of Asia."

While Alexander lost himself in the crowd, Timothy turned to James and said:

"I fear some plot against Paul from that evil-minded Alexander."

"They would not dare to profane the Temple by seizing him while he is fulfilling the days of his vows," James replied, as they went on their way.

On Pentecost, May 28, 57 A.D., while crowds of worshipers were thronging the entrances and courts of the Temple, Paul was conducting along the streets the four men who had been assigned to him by James to the registry for sacrifices. One of the men was smooth-shaven because he was from another country. In passing the home of his sister, Paul had the four men wait while he called upon her to tell her that as soon as his days of purification were completed, and the sacrifice made, he would come to visit with her. Alexander had other men following Paul, who were not well enough

acquainted with Trophimus to identify him. They lost
sight of Paul and his associates in the crowd, but,
diligently watching, they again recognized him in the
Temple, when the seven days were almost completed.
They came to the outer courts and declared that Paul
had taken a Greek, who was not a Jew, into the Temple,
in violation of the warnings at every entrance.

These men who had been urged on by Alexander
raised the cry that aroused every Jew in hearing:

"Men of Israel, help."

"This man, Paul, not only preaches against the law,
but he has brought a Greek into the Temple to defile it,"
they shouted.

The word was shouted along, even to the streets, and
a great mob gathered, while Paul and his companions
were at their devotions in the Temple. Alexander
joined the crowd, but from his experience in Ephesus
he did not push himself forward as a leader. The mob
rushed into the Temple and, forgetting that the offense
could only be committed by one not a Jew, they seized
Paul. They pulled him along the floor, down the steps,
through the courts, and down the outside steps, tearing off
his clothing and bruising his body, wounding his face so that
trickling blood matted his beard. Outside the Temple,
gaining his feet, he demanded to know what was his offense.

Alexander, seeing the helpless state of Paul, came
close to him, shouting, "Apostate," and spat in Paul's
face. So quickly that Alexander did not know what had
happened, Paul struck out and laid him low. He turned
on others, striking at them, felling them until there was
a clear space around him. The Roman officer with the
guard had seen the valiant defense, but it was his duty

to arrest the man whom all seemed to accuse, some of one thing and some of another.   He led Paul to the tower of Antonia; and Paul, turning to the howling mob following, spoke in the Aramaic, to their surprise.   He recounted his experience on the way to Damascus, and held the mob in close attention until he told them that he had been commanded to carry the word to the Gentiles.   At that their old fury broke out.

The Roman centurion took Paul into the tower, to prevent the mob from injuring him, and then directed that he should be flogged to compel a confession.   Paul's instant claim of Roman citizenship stopped the officer, who reported the claims of Paul to Claudius Lysias, the military tribune.

Claudius Lysias treated Paul with the consideration due a Roman citizen.   He took him before the Sanhedrin the next day to find out what was the charge.

When Paul declared before the council that he had lived before God in all good conscience, the high priest Ananias commanded the guards to smite him on the mouth.   With all his pride offended, Paul retorted:

"God shall smite you, you whited wall."

Reminded that he should not revile the high priest, Paul with fine sarcasm replied:

"I could not know that he was the high priest."

The council was united against Paul, but, knowing the fierce partisanship of the sects, he adroitly set the factions against each other by saying:

"I am a Pharisee of a long line of Pharisees.   Because of my hope of the resurrection I am accused."

Immediately the factions set at each other so fiercely that Claudius Lysias sent guards to take Paul away, fearing he would be torn to pieces. That night Paul had a vision bidding him be of good cheer, that he should bear witness of his Master in Rome.

Alexander, in a meeting with some Jews known as dagger men, was telling them many stories about Paul in Asia, and he persuaded them to bind themselves under an oath to slay Paul when he should be brought before the council on pretense of further examination. Ahiram, Paul's beloved nephew, heard the plot and, hastening with fresh clothing to Paul, told him of the plot. Paul had his nephew tell the story to Claudius Lysias, who immediately made preparations and sent Paul by night under safe guards to Felix, the procurator in Caesarea, with a letter stating the case.

Felix was an avaricious officer who could not conceal the low estate of a slave from which he had risen. When Paul had been presented before him, he made careful inquiry of what province Paul was, and his time-serving retainers learned that Paul had brought a large sum of money to Jerusalem for charity. Felix gave time for Ananias and his special-pleading lawyer, Tertullus, to appear and prosecute. Tertullus fawned on Felix, but the procurator knew that there was no money to be gained from the high priest's party. The lawyer made serious and eloquent charges that Paul was stirring up trouble among the Jews throughout the world. He tried to force Felix to put Paul to inquisition, to discover the proof of his charges.

Paul denied the charges and defied his accusers to produce any proof. He aroused the cupidity of Felix by stating that not over twelve days before he had passed through Caesarea on his way to Jerusalem, bearing alms to his countrymen in that city. He surveyed the accusers who had come down with the high priest, as if looking for someone; then, looking the high priest significantly in the eye, he said:

"There were certain Jews from Asia who ought to have been here."

Paul began an explanation of the teachings of the Way, but Felix said that he understood the teaching very well.

Felix seemed indifferent to the accusations and yet he wanted to hold Paul. He brought the hearing to an end, so far as the accusers were concerned.

"When Lysias shall come down, I will determine your matter," said Felix to Paul. Then, turning to the lictors, he said:

"Keep him nominally in the praetorium, but with privileges; permit him to visit and to receive his friends."

In a few days Felix, scheming to procure some payment by Paul or his friends for release, had him brought up as if for hearing as to his faith. Felix and his wife, Drusilla, sat in the hall of hearing, in all the pomp of the procurator's station, to receive Paul. She was the sister of Agrippa II and of Berenice. While she was the wife of Azizus, king of Emesa, she yielded to the praises of Felix, left her husband, and allied herself with Felix. She was a Jewess. Paul saw the insincerity of Felix and the vain curiosity of Drusilla.

Paul's fearless exposition of righteousness, condemnation of yielding to lust, and his attack upon lawlessness so terrified Felix and Drusilla that Felix dismissed him. Often he sent his emissaries to suggest to Paul and his friends that the payment of money would release him.

After being detained in Caesarea for three months, Paul was surprised by a visit from his brother David.

Paul was anxious about home affairs, he was getting along to that age when the memories of his youth were dear to him. David told him that his father had been buried in the early spring; and, after long hesitation, David told him that Deborah, his mother, had passed on, leaving a last word for her son, Saul. According to David's report, Ben Hanan had softened toward Saul in his last years, and had told the elders of the congregation of the Way in Tarsus that he wanted them to know that as much faith as they had in their doctrines, he had more in his son, Saul, who could not have been wholly wrong.

"And mother said to tell you," David spoke brokenly, "that all these years she has believed that every word you spoke was inspired, and that your Master will welcome her in the resurrection."

The two men sat long in silence, solemnly communing with sacred memories.

"Mother bade me give you Tabitha's wedding ring," said David, taking the treasure from his girdle and giving it to Paul.

While Paul gazed fondly upon the ring, his lips were forming words unspoken; but a lovelight was in his eyes that disclosed the tenderness of his memories.

"Father's last request was that as soon as I could, I should convert your interests in the business into cash, and that your interest should be reckoned the same as if you had been actively in the business all the time. That I have done and have letters of credit for you," said David, taking from his girdle a wallet.

"This I cannot take," said Paul. "I have not helped you in all these years. No, it must not be so."

"Would you refuse the gift from him whose last act was in atonement?" David asked. "He feared that if it were left to me to make the division you would refuse it, but he said you could not refuse it from him, as his dying gift of slight reparation."

"But I have been bitter. You take it; give it to the poor in Tarsus," said Paul, in his confusion.

"And I promised our father," continued David, "that I would convince you that it was best for you to take this yourself. It could never be more timely than in the present case, when you are held prisoner."

During the conversation David had been holding the wallet, containing the letters of credit, open before Paul, who took it as if it were a hallowed memento. Then the stalwart David bowed his head, while the elder brother, with his hand on David's head, pronounced a blessing.

The detention of Paul lengthened into months, even to two years. During that time he was not compelled to remain in the praetorium, but he was permitted to live with his friends. Once in a while Felix would have him returned to the praetorium and then an agent would appear to suggest the payment of money for a release. To every demand of Paul for a trial, Felix would make excuse that he could not fix a time that would suit his convenience and the presence of Claudius Lysias.

The list of extortions and reckless indulgences of Felix culminated in his immediate recall to Rome. Learning that Felix was about to leave, Alexander hastened down to Caesarea and convinced him that it would enlist the aid of the Jews, if he would imprison Paul, so that the succeeding procurator would be compelled to deal with the case.

CHAPTER XXXVIII

TO CAESAR

Porcius Festus succeeded Felix in July, 59 A.D., and found Paul in prison, under charges made two years before. He was anxious to dispose of the case quickly to avoid any scandal likely connected with it. Festus went up to Jerusalem to learn the details of the case. The wily Ananias urged Festus to send Paul back to Jerusalem for trial; and, believing that that would be done, Alexander collected the dagger men, among whom were the men who, two years before, had sworn to slay Paul. They plotted to kill him on the way up from Caesarea. After a few days, Festus set out for Caesarea, accompanied by leading men of the Sanhedrin. He was anxious to please the Jews.

Paul was brought before the new procurator; and immediately, the Jews, who had come down, began making different charges against him. Paul vehemently denied the charges of any wrong against Caesar or the laws of the Jews. Then Festus proposed that Paul go up to Jerusalem and be tried before him there.

With fine scorn Paul declared that he stood before a court of Rome where he, as a Roman citizen, had a right to be judged; that he could not be given up to be tried by the Jews.

"I appeal to Caesar," Paul said, impressively.

Festus suddenly realized that he had been led into a false position with a man above the average in intelligence.

He conferred with his counselors, then said:

"Unto Caesar you shall go."

Agrippa II, with his sister Berenice, was making a tour of display and inspection throughout the regions over which he was king. He had been favored by the powers of Rome because, in that city, he had ingratiated himself with influential men. His family, from Herod the Great, had always been strong supporters of Roman rule, although they had embraced the Jewish faith in outward semblance. It was well known at the time that Agrippa was living in his palace in Caesarea Philippi with his sister Berenice, as if she were his wife. Agrippa and Berenice, in great pomp, visited Festus shortly after Paul's hearing, and Festus asked the king for advice as to the charges to be sent up with Paul on his appeal; for he did not want Rome to laugh at him for sending up an improper case.

When Agrippa and Berenice had retired to their chambers in the palace, a slave gave her a letter.

"From whom is the letter?" Agrippa asked.

"It is from our sister, Drusilla," said Berenice, while reading. "She says they have been ordered to Rome to answer charges and she asks us to send her letters to help her and Felix."

"As if we could help," said Agrippa, despondently, "living as we are."

"Why be ashamed," said Berenice. "Marriage laws and rules are good for the people, but not necessary for rulers. Cleopatra married her brother, and rulers have always, in such things, been a law unto themselves. Besides, the time may come when some Roman of influence will desire me, and then we will not have to be divorced. Life is as you live it, and conscience is of your own making."

At a sumptuous banquet that evening, Agrippa told Festus that he would like to hear Paul himself, and Berenice added that Drusilla said he was almost a magician.

Festus arranged an elaborate ceremony in the hall of judgment the next day. Soldiers escorted Agrippa, Berenice, Festus, and his wife to seats on the dais; the fasces were there in burnished brightness; rugs of elaborate design covered the steps and the dais. Paul, in chains, was brought before them and the assembled officers, with an audience of prominent citizens, making use of the occasion to pay honor to Agrippa. Then Festus made a speech, saying that his reason for the hearing was that he might know what to write to Caesar.

"Wherefore, I have brought him before you, King Agrippa," said Festus.

Upon Agrippa giving Paul permission to speak, the apostle changed the whole aspect in a moment by assuming the attitude of one who was master, although courteously paying tribute to the office held by Agrippa. In an adroit compliment to Agrippa's knowledge as a Jew, he made the king judge of the things involved in the story of Paul's life, and made his appeal to the righteousness taught in the law. He knew that the king was a Pharisee, and, after presenting his own claims to that sect, he swept the king on to the resurrection, saying: "Why is it judged incredible with you, if God does raise the dead?"

Then he hurried on to the story of his own life in persecuting the saints and his experience on the road to

Damascus. He repeated that story vividly. Agrippa and those with him forgot their own doubts and in awe listened to the orator, who made them see the vision as he had seen it. He told them of the commission to him, in that vision, to take the glad tidings to all Jews, and even to the Gentiles; then, rising to the loftiest heights of eloquence, he cried out:

"I stand unto this day, testifying both to small and great, how that the Christ first by the resurrection of the dead should proclaim light both to the Jews and to the Gentiles."

Festus interrupted to tell Paul that he was mad, in fact, to make him remember that he was a prisoner. Paul courteously answered that he was not mad. Then he said that the king knew all these things.

Agrippa had forgotten his kingly pose. Berenice paled under the condemnation of that conscience she had denied. Paul sensed the situation and like a flash of judgment he said abruptly:

"King Agrippa, do you believe the prophets?"

The king was confused, Berenice was in worse state. Before the king could make answer, Paul clinched the indictment before the court of conscience by saying:

"I know that you believe."

Agrippa dared not deny his belief. He recovered his composure by strong will-power, laughed in the cynical manner he had learned in Rome and said:

"With so little persuasion, would you make me a Christian?"

"Would to God that not only you but all who hear me," said Paul, in such impressive manner that reply was impossible, "might become such as I am," and

I KNOW THAT YOU BELIEVE

stretching out his manacled arms, he said in a whisper reaching everyone in the room, "except these bonds."

An awkward pause followed. All arose and followed the military escort out of the hall. The guards were puzzled to know what to do with Paul, for there had been no decision. A lictor advised them to take him back to his cell.

When Paul learned that he was to be taken to Italy by Julius, a centurion, he made all arrangements with his friends for his departure. Julius told him that the ship would be crowded, but that if he had any servants, he might take two of them along. Thus it was that Luke and Aristarchus were listed as servants of Paul and taken with him to Rome, although Julius knew them well. Agrippa had said to the centurion:

"This man Paul might have been discharged if he had not appealed to Caesar. See that your soldiers do not mistreat him, and that you give him fair treatment."

The guards of the praetorium permitted all privileges to Paul and his friends. When Julius came to take Paul to the ship, he laughed tolerantly at the guard, bunglingly slipping the chains on Paul in bringing him to the centurion; and then Julius took off the chains and handed them back to the guard.

It was in August, 59 A.D., that Paul, with Luke and Aristarchus, set sail from Caesarea under the guard of Julius, who was taking other prisoners to Rome. At Sidon, 70 miles north, they stopped for a week to unload and reload, during which time Julius permitted Paul to go ashore among his friends. In contrary winds they made their way to Myra of Lycia. There Julius transferred his prisoners to an Egyptian grain ship, bound for Italy, a much larger ship on which there were 276 passengers, besides a cargo.

The ship sailed close to the coast to gain the help of land breezes until it reached opposite Cnidus; and then tried to sail close to the wind from the west, which drove the ship south to Crete. Sailing along the southern shore of Crete, the ship reached Fair Havens. It was now early October and nearing the season when navigation would be suspended, from November until February.

When a wind came from the south the master of the ship persuaded Julius, over Paul's protest from his experience as a traveler, to put to sea to reach Phoenix, only 50 miles away, because the harbor in Fair Havens was not suitable for wintering. Suddenly a northeast wind, called the Euraquilo, burst down on them and drove them to the little island of Cauda. Under the lee of Cauda, the sailors took on deck the boat in tow, and undergirded the leaking ship by ropes passed around it midship and tightened by a capstan. They lowered the sail, fearing they would be driven on the dangerous sands off the African coast, and struggled to keep the ship headed to the northwest. While they drifted, they threw over the spars and tackling of the ship. Neither stars nor sun shone for many days. Paul cheered the men when they were in panic, saying that his God in a vision had told him that no life would be lost, although the ship would be.

After fourteen days of imminent peril, without sight of land or of sun or stars, the sailors heard the boom of waves on a coast line; and at midnight, by sounding, they found they were approaching a coast. Panic seized some of the sailors, who, under pretense of laying out anchors, tried to launch the small boat; and Paul notified Julius, who had soldiers cut away the ropes and let the small boat go adrift.

In the early morning Paul heartened the passengers by his calm manner, taking bread, blessing it as was his custom, and persuading all to eat. They threw overboard the jars of grain in the hold, to lighten the ship, for they were coming to a strange coast at daylight. They cut loose the anchors, which had been let out from the stern of the ship, unloosed the rudders for use, and, setting the small sail at the bow, they steered the ship for a sandy beach. The soldiers, fearing the penalty for allowing prisoners to escape, wanted to kill the prisoners; but Julius, on account of his friendship for Paul, refused to allow the slaying of the prisoners.

Paul, along with those who could swim, leaped overboard, and others, clinging to wreckage, for the ship was now going to pieces, made their way to land, where they learned they were on the island of Melita (Malta). The survivors shivered from the cold November wind. The natives built fires and Paul brought fagots to lay on the fire. A serpent among the fagots was warmed to life and fastened on Paul's hand, terrifying the natives; but he shook it off without it doing him any harm. The natives had at first thought he was a criminal, but now that he suffered no harm from the serpent, they thought he was a god.

Paul and his companions were taken and housed by Publius, the governor of the island, for three days. While there Paul restored the father of Publius whom Luke, the physician, pronounced to be suffering from fever and dysentery. The news of this restoration spread through the island, so that, during the three months they stayed there, the people brought their sick to be cured.

In February, 60 A.D., Julius engaged passage for his prisoners on the Alexandrian ship, Dioscuri (Twin Brothers), which had wintered at Melita. They reached Puteoli, a seaport for ships in the Egyptian trade, although it was 100 miles to Rome by the Appian Way.

During the seven days of waiting at Puteoli for escort of the prisoners, Julius permitted Paul to hunt up and visit with his brethren. Paul was filled with misgivings as to the outcome of his trial; and they increased when he learned that the year before Nero had started on his bloody career by having his mother, Agrippina, assassinated.

The news that Paul was on his way to Rome as a prisoner was sent ahead of him; and Christians came to meet him at the Market of Appius and at the Three Taverns, welcoming him with demonstrations of joy.

"Am I merely a military escort of a returning commander or am I to deliver you as prisoner?" said Julius in good humor to Paul.

"I am an ambassador in chains," Paul replied.

CHAPTER XXXIX

BUSY IN CHAINS

Julius, arriving with his prisoners in Rome, took all except Paul to the centurion Longinus, who had general supervision of the Praetorian Guard. All his prisoners had been accounted for and checked from his list, save Paul.

"Where is this Paul of Tarsus?" Longinus asked.

"He is waiting with some of his friends on the outside, until I call him," Julius replied.

"You officers in the provinces are entirely too trusting; you know the penalty is your life, if he escapes," said Longinus.

"And he has had my life in his keeping," replied Julius. "It was his calmness and wisdom that saved us in a shipwreck; he healed the father of Publius in Melita; he was two years on his honor, waiting for trial before Felix; and Festus does not send up any charge that can be a violation of the Roman law. It is something about Jewish law. Agrippa asked me to extend him every favor. I have given him liberty at seaports in his own country and here in Italy. He has a high sense of honor, and he is a most interesting man."

"Let us go to Burrus, the prefect of the Praetorian Guard, who yet rules for Nero," said Longinus. "Tell your prisoner where you have gone, lest he get lost in trying to find you."

Julius, laughing at the humor of Longinus, went to the entrance to the Praetorian Camp, where Paul was holding a reception to many friends coming to meet him. The centurion told Paul to await his return, for he hoped to avoid taking him to the cells.

When Julius and Longinus appeared before Burrus, they found there Seneca, the tutor of Nero and associate with Burrus in administering civil government. These two administered the details of government and were the advisers of the emperor, until a fews year later, when Nero could not brook any advice contrary to his desires.

Longinus said, "Julius has a prisoner from Caesarea, who has come with such high recommendation that I fear we will have to send Julius to jail with him. Let Julius tell the story."

Then Julius rehearsed all the history he had of the case, and he told them of the great help Paul had been in saving the passengers, and that he had been given plenty of opportunity to escape, long before he had been turned over to him.

"For two years Felix held him on honor that he would not leave Caesarea; and, when Felix left on summons to Rome, he placed Paul in prison to satisfy some Jews."

"If this man has been under the custody of Felix for two years," said Burrus in gruff honesty, "he has suffered enough humiliation to expiate any crime, short of treason."

"I feel interested in this man," said Seneca, "for I read a letter he wrote to his followers here that displays deep knowledge of the foundation of morals."

"I know him well," spoke up Gallio, who was visiting his brother Seneca. "There is a class of Jews opposing him, and many Jews and others believe in him implicitly. He will die rather than violate his pledge. I knew him in Tarsus as a lad, and again I met him in that miserable, sickly Corinth, when I was proconsul there."

"Receipt Julius for him," said Burrus to Longinus, "and parole him on honor." Noticing Seneca lift his eyebrow suggestively, Burrus added, "And furnish him with a guard in his house, the expense of which he must bear; otherwise, he must be confined, however meritorious his case."

When Julius met Longinus later, he asked him what had been done with the prisoner, Paul.

"He has hired a house and I have agreed to detail a guard from day to day for him," said Longinus. "He is a most delightful gentleman; made me feel sorry that I had to be even as exacting as that. I am going to hear him talk to the people he has invited. Very interesting man."

Paul first sent for the Jews of the city; but, because they were divided in opinion, he invited the Gentiles. His days were filled with activity. Guards eagerly sought the assignment to watch over him. Day by day he expounded the life of Jesus, and showed how it was an appeal to every man as an individual. Officers of the Praetorian Guard came to listen, and their friends counted it a favor to accompany them. There was a simplicity in the morals that Paul taught, a stern uprightness demanded by him, that aroused the vanishing integrity and rigid morality once taught by Cato and the honored men of Rome. Slaves slipped in to hear the words of cheer; women, whose burdens were heavy, found strength to bear them in the love of the Christ.

The most arduous of Paul's labors was to advise the men he sent out as heralds over the lands; for all of his old, faithful associates (and, daily, new converts) came and went on missions. He composed letters in the hearing of audiences crowding his hired house. He explained how he was trying to keep the congregations to the simplicity of the faith, and to prevent the grafting on it of any Jewish customs or the merging of it with other religions. His guard would often neglect to place the manacle on his wrist, linking him to the guard. He was no longer the herald; he was now the leader, the organizer; for men came from Colossae, from Macedonia, from Asia, and from all over the country, to be instructed how to organize the congregations, and to settle the questions arising in every section. Prominent people listened and believed. Longinus often took his friends to hear Paul dictate some of his letters.

A poor slave, Onesimus, hearing the words of love, confessed that he had stolen what he thought he had earned from Philemon, his master, a friend of Paul in Colossae, and had spent it in riotous living in Rome.

"What can I, a despised Phrygian slave, hope for?" Onesimus cried, groveling at Paul's feet.

"It is simple," said Paul. "Let him that stole, steal no more. You are now a brother. What matters it that you are a slave under these laws? You are free, because your soul is free."

Paul dictated a letter for Timothy to write to Philemon, pledging himself to pay whatever the slave failed to pay, signing it himself; and gave it to Onesimus to take to his master. The Roman officers marveled that Paul's words could inspire lowly men with such lofty ideals and at the same time hold patricians spellbound.

After Paul had been in custody over a year, Burrus came one day with a friend whom he did not introduce, who was intensely interested in Paul's teaching. Paul made an earnest request that some time be set for his hearing.

"I do not see the need of delaying longer," said Burrus, "but things seem changed in Jerusalem, so that we get no news about accusers being sent."

"However, you forget," said the companion of Burrus, "that Poppaea Sabina, the favored mistress, has asked the emperor that the hearing be postponed until the full limit of two years for accusers to appear, because she has embraced the Jewish faith."

"That has its influence, but I will not wait longer than that period, as a matter of justice," said Burrus. "How much longer will we have to endure this degradation?"

"Perhaps not long," said the visitor, whimsically, "for Nero does not hesitate to ask leading men to open their veins."

When Burrus and his companion had left, Urbanus told Paul that the visitor with Burrus was the famous Seneca, the teacher and philosopher, who was the civil administrator under the emperor.

CHAPTER XL

BORN A GENTLEMAN

In Jerusalem conditions had changed. The continual agitation of the Jews against Rome made it necessary for Agrippa to exercise his full authority, by deposing Ananias and appointing Ismael high priest. Ananias had grown wealthy and still exercised a considerable influence in opposition to Agrippa. The time, two years, in which accusers must appear against Paul would soon expire. Alexander went to Agrippa with a plea that he should send accusers, or authorize them to be sent, to Rome.

"It is no affair of Roman law," said Agrippa, "and if any accusers go, they must be sent by the Sanhedrin."

"It is not any concern of my administration," said the high priest, Ismael, in answer to Alexander's request to send witnesses. "You and Ananias were the principal ones stirring up the trouble against Paul; now complete your plans."

Alexander called on Ananias, who had retired to his richly furnished home to enjoy his wealth.

"The time will soon be gone in which we can appear against Paul," Alexander urged to Ananias.

"I am without power," said Ananias. "Agrippa has stripped me of all influence, even denying me the rights of a past high priest."

"Use your own wealth; finance me and the witnesses I will get," Alexander insinuatingly argued, "and the Jews who taunt you with having made money out of

your office will be silenced.   More than that, I will prove
that Paul is against Rome, and I will tell the emperor
that you, out of your loyalty to him, even against
Agrippa, sent us there to save the power of Rome.   This
would undermine Agrippa and reinstate you in your office out of the emperor's gratitude."

"But there is the expense," Ananias urged.

"But the satisfaction there would be in overcoming
this ambitious Paul, and in replacing you as high priest,"
urged Alexander.   "And I must start at once to reach
Rome before the seas are closed by the winter season.
It is now late."

Ananias studied long in silence; then he went to a
secret panel in the walls of the room and took out a
purse, which he handed to Alexander, saying:

"See to your witnesses, for Paul is skilful.   Come
when you are ready to start and I will give you letters to
men in Rome, vouching for you and your friends."

Thus it was that Alexander, with witnesses, departed
for Rome, but he was so delayed in getting transportation along the coast to a place where he could find a ship
bound for Rome, that he, with his prepared witnesses,
took passage from Antioch on the last ship sailing before
the winter season.   A Jewish writer says that no one
was saved from the wreck of that ship, although more
than two hundred were aboard.   The vessel was driven
out of its course and wrecked off the coast of Melita.
One survivor, Alexander, was washed ashore, lashed to
a spar; but he was lost for so long a time and was so
discouraged in seeking identification, that he feared to
make himself known in Jerusalem.   His funds and letters
were lost.   When he recovered consciousness on the

sands of the beach, he felt a strange thrill, as if new life had come to him.

The natives in pity took Alexander to Publius to whom the former told his mission. The winter season was now on. A ship was in port, waiting for spring to open. Publius shrewdly refrained from telling Alexander that he knew Paul, and refused to give him permission to sail on the first ship, which left in February, giving the excuse that it was loaded to capacity. It was late in April when another ship bound for Puteoli touched at Melita, and Publius permitted Alexander to sail on it.

Meanwhile, the hired house in which Paul held forth had become a resort for the learned and the common people. He had gathered around him a large number of helpers, some of whom had been with him through Asia and Macedonia and Greece, others who had been with him on his long journeys and while he held his school for two years in Ephesus. They relieved the tedium of teaching the new attendants. They organized the believers in congregations, after the manner of the democracy of the synagogue; they helped select trustworthy overseers, who had supervision over the congregations in the country to which they were assigned. Paul was not content to have mere allegiance to him, but his desire was to establish growing and perpetuating bodies.

Rome became the center of the new movement. Paul was delighted that an increasing interest was spreading the glad tidings over the world. There was no ritual provided; but Luke, poet, physician, and painter, had prepared hymns expressing the divine origin of their belief, their hopes and their gratitude, which were chanted with heartfelt enthusiasm by the followers. While the leaders were discussing the necessity of keeping the story of Jesus free from future mistakes, Paul said:

"Luke should preserve those two hymns of his, the one that expresses our adoration and the one that is a holy benediction."

"What appeal will this religion have after you are gone?" Longinus asked, after Paul had made that statement.

"The appeal that there is in the life and divinity of Jesus," Paul answered. "His life is not for one people, nor for any limited number of generations. He touches humanity in every phase and under all conditions, in all times and lands, because he is the Spirit of Love and Truth."

"How shall we know those who are his followers?" Longinus urged.

"By the manner of their lives, and not by their names," Paul replied; and, noticing several patricians with Longinus puzzling over the answer, he added, "Jesus has said that not everyone that calls him Lord shall enter in, but believers in him will show their love without hypocrisy; they will abhor that which is evil, seek that which is good; they will be honest and loyal citizens of their own land; compassionate with those who sin, in weakness or ignorance; and they will always be sweetly reasonable. They are not less, but more efficient, citizens of their country, in the everyday affairs of life."

"Seems impossible that men can reach that superior state," Longinus said.

"They may not, owing to human imperfection; but the distinctive characteristic of the lover of Jesus is that he is striving to that end," said Paul.

"Since no man can be perfect," Longinus urged, on the whispered suggestion of a patrician, "how is a man to know that he has been received, or is acceptable?"

"Easily; however great the sins forgiven him, or the faults he must overcome, his witness is not someone outside of himself," said Paul. "The Spirit itself bears witness with our spirit, that we are the children of God."

Longinus and his friends had nothing more to say, but left, shaking their heads in doubt and discussing the matter solemnly among themselves.

From early morning until the oil burned low in the flickering lamps, great and small, strong and weak, rich and poor, heard from Paul the tidings that gave them hope and love. They learned that the Christ-spirit came to heal and bind up the spiritual wounds of everyone and to give him the courage to struggle, to sacrifice, and truly to enjoy living. The hours of every day were too short for Paul to tell the wondrous power of the glad tidings to bring forth and increase spirituality in men and women.

The last of the days in which Paul could be held, awaiting accusers, had passed; and he was brought before Burrus in his council-room. Burrus had summoned Felix to be present, out of caution, so that the discredited procurator could not make it an occasion for an appeal to Poppaea, to excite her growing animosity toward Seneca and himself.

"Felix, it appears that this prisoner was left by you in prison; and that Festus, your successor, has sent him treated generously, and I thank God for the friends I have been given in Rome; but while there is vigor in my body, I must travel with this message to other countries. I bid you farewell."

"That man was born a gentleman," said Seneca, as Paul left the chamber. "He reminds me over and over of the admonition of the wise Athenodorus, 'So live with men, as if God saw you; so speak with God, as if men were listening.' He has no fear, because his soul is free."

After a season of rejoicing and preparation, Paul summoned his friends to bid them farewell, saying:

"I am going to a strange field, the farther limits of the west, to take to those who have never heard it the story of the Life, Crucifixion, and Resurrection of Jesus. I will take Luke with me, and if it be that my life shall pay the price, it will be a small sacrifice compared with the suffering of Jesus to bring to me and all men the way of salvation, for our spiritual lives are of greater moment than the physical lives we have to live. You will have our beloved Mark with you, to whose loyalty I testify in the sweet forgetfulness of past differences, to keep you in the faith delivered to you. My own funds have failed, but the contributions of the brothers in Macedonia and Asia are sufficient. The work is now in your hands. May Jesus, our Lord and Master, keep you in his everlasting love. Farewell!"

In a few days, the early spring of 62 A.D., Paul and Luke, having been accompanied to the coast by a host of friends, set sail on their journey from Rome to the principal cities of Spain.

here on his appeal," said Burrus, before speakin
Paul. "Do you know of any offense that he has
mitted against Rome?"

"None," replied Felix. "I was compelled to
him because of the insistence of leaders of the Sanhed
that he taught a doctrine that was against their faitl

"Then why did you not release him?" Burrus aske

"Because I feared," said Felix, "that they migl
complain of me."

"Have you any charges to prefer, or testimony t
give against him?" Burrus asked severely.

"Assuredly not. I know that his doctrine is not a
menace to Rome," said Felix frankly. "In fact, I
feared that he would complain against me."

"That is not my affair," said Paul. "I am not
concerned with laws and their administration, but I am
interested in the welfare of men."

"No one having appeared against you," said Burrus
to Paul, "it is my duty to release you. I take this
opportunity to thank you for the splendid lessons of
morality which you have given to our soldiers and
citizens, something we very much need. I do not know
that I accept, or wholly reject, the faith which you
teach; but I pay my respects to the honesty of your
purpose and the purity in the lives of men and women
alike, that your teaching demands. My associate here,"
he turned to Seneca, who remained silent, "is in happy
accord with all that I have said. You are now free to
remain in the city on account of your age, or to go."

"The charge against me was absurd and untrue, but
I do not hold the officers responsible," said Paul, with a
courtesy as if he were himself a patrician. "I have been

CHAPTER XLI

AGAIN IN PRISON

Alexander, upon his arrival in Rome, hunted up Felix and Drusilla and tried to enlist them in his cause.

"I have a dim recollection of a man by the name of Alexander, who came down from Jerusalem with the principal men, when Paul was brought before me," said Felix to Alexander, "but he was an older man than you seem to be, and that was four years ago."

"But do you not remember me, when I came down just before you left, and advised you to put Paul in prison; that it would make the Jews your friends?" Alexander asked. But Felix not showing any sign of recognition, Alexander urged, "I started from Jerusalem with witnesses who would have convicted him, but I am the only survivor of the shipwreck. I can still make good my promise to help you."

"I am not concerned with any prosecution," said Felix, "for I have my own affairs to look after and Jews are not helpful, in the courts of Rome."

"At least, identify me before the magistrates," Alexander urged, "for I lost all my papers in the shipwreck."

"I have told you that I could not make good identification," said Felix. "Besides, Paul was released and left the city almost two months ago."

The coppersmith was without friends, although he met many he had known in Corinth and Ephesus who seemed to doubt him and failed to recognize him.

Often he looked in a mirror to find a strange face reflected, although it was his own; but he saw there was an expression, as if a few lines of youth had been grafted on an old face. His eyes were still old and sinister, in contrast to the younger lines. He laughed, speaking aloud to himself:

"So this is my curse, to live. It shall be a blessing."

He found that whatever of youth had been restored to him separated him from his former acquaintances, and that he had to seek new friends and had to establish a personality, which his mixture of youth and age made impossible. He could not return to Jerusalem, for they would not believe him; nor could he go to Corinth or Ephesus, for the same reason, and because he had not accomplished any of his boasts to remove Paul. He had to take up his life in Rome; and yet, moved by his long hate against Paul, he found a little satisfaction in spying on the Christians.

The great fire in Rome, breaking out July 19, 64 A.D., raged for six days, destroying the portions of the city where Nero had desired to build wonderful works of art. The part of the city occupied by the Jews strangely escaped, although exposed. The populace immediately muttered that Nero had set the fire. Then friends of the emperor pointed to the fact that the Jews had escaped, as proof that the Jews had set the fire. There were many Jews who had advanced funds to Nero in his profligate expenditure, to tide him over until taxes would be returned, for the senate servilely voted any allowance that he asked. A close friend of the emperor, who had met Alexander, suggested that the Christians had started the fire. Alexander spread this false story,

eagerly accepted, and for a time it was sufficient to allay
the murmurings of the populace.

When the explanation offered was about to lose its
force, Nero seized on it to give himself full exoneration.
To divert the minds of the public from the charges against
him, he caused the Christians to be taken; and with
short shrift they were condemned to furnish the rare
spectacle of human torches along the pillared walks;
they were fed to wild beasts in the arena, until even the
lust of Rome for blood was satiated, disgusted. But Nero
could not understand that any passion could be satisfied.

Many Christians fled in terror from Rome, while
brave ones remained, to comfort and succor the families
of their unfortunate brothers. They met in subter-
ranean rooms, in the catacombs, in half-destroyed
buildings, guarded by an outpost to give them warning
of the approach of their enemies.

Alexander kept in close touch with the Christians
and found many of their places of meeting. He learned
that if one, not personally known to the guard, made
a figure of a fish in the dust, or traced it out on a wall,
he was admitted or directed where to go to meet the
Christians.

The active persecution of the Christians had subsided, except in the provinces. The years were passing,
and in the meetings, once in a great while, Alexander
learned of the journeys of Paul: that he was in Dalmatia,
or that he had been in Crete; that he was in Laodicea
and on his way for a brief visit to Colossae; but always
the news was so late that Paul would have left the city
from which the news came, before anyone could arrive
from Rome.

Alexander had followed his trade as coppersmith and his spying for four years. He did not care to report upon the ordinary members he found in the meetings of the Christians. He was embittered against Paul, because he felt that Paul was the principal agency in exalting the life of the Crucified One. His many failures to accomplish his revenge on Paul only served to increase his desire, now grown to an obsession.

Nero had spent much of his time and had almost taken up his permanent residence in Corinth, where he was concerned in constructing a canal across the isthmus and in winning crowns in the Isthmian games, by the simple expedient of demanding the punishment of anyone who dared to defeat him. He indulged the fancy that he was a musician and an actor who could restore the old Greek drama. In the distant provinces of Rome rebellions were fomenting.

Alexander heard that Paul was growing old rapidly; and, after specially strenuous activities, that in the autumn of 66 A.D. he was going to Nicopolis of Epirus, the memorial city built by Augustus, overlooking a small bay on the gulf of Arta, to spend the winter there.

Seneca and Burrus, earnest and honest advisers of Nero, had been dismissed. Nymphidius Sabinus and Sofonus Tigellinus had been appointed as administrators in Rome, chiefly because they fawningly served Nero and obeyed every venal and egotistic whim of the degenerating emperor. Tigellinus, having many plans of his own to carry out, followed Nero to Corinth. Helius, a freedman, often discharged the duties of Sabinus in Rome.

Drusilla had found favor with some of the influential men, because she had the favor of Poppaea, who had now become the wife of Nero; and Poppaea was pleased to extend some favors to Drusilla, on account of the Jewish religion, which she had embraced. Felix was scheming to regain, through the questionable influence of his wife, Drusilla, his standing in the government. These conditions were known to Alexander and he went to Felix with the news he had of Paul. He came to the house of Felix at the very moment that Drusilla was upbraiding her husband with demanding that she make every sacrifice to win the senators to a favorable report on his case, while he did nothing himself.

"You refused to identify me," said Alexander, when admitted to the presence of Felix and Drusilla, "but that was because—well, a change—no matter—that is past. You know that I know all that Alexander knew. I have not been idle these four years. I have witnesses that will swear that Paul has spent all these years since his release in speaking against the rule of Rome. I know where he is hiding, in Nicopolis, in easy reach of Brundisium. They have killed many of his deluded followers, but why not take Paul, the man responsible for all this turmoil? If you go to the magistrates with this information, you will have a strong claim upon the friends of the emperor."

"Why do you hesitate?" said Drusilla, petulantly. "Helius, a freedman like yourself, ought to be willing to help you, and he acts for Sabinus in all things. You urge me to claim religion with Poppaea, now you should claim the ties between two men who came from the same station."

Drusilla had lost her fear of Felix along with her respect for him, since he had thrown her into the arms of senators.

When Felix, with Alexander, appeared before Helius, asking that Paul be brought from Nicopolis on a charge of disloyalty, because he was a leader of the proscribed sect, Helius demanded that the man Alexander should lead officers where they could make arrests of Christians meeting secretly, so that it would not appear as if only one man were being singled out. He slyly urged that if it became necessary to show any leniency, there would be plenty of subjects to be released without releasing the man Paul.

"I am pleased that you have brought this about," said Helius with a smirk to Felix. "By catching the leader, we may relieve ourselves of passing sentence on so many sobbing women and martyr-like men."

Much against his will, Alexander was compelled to betray a gathering of Christians to the Roman guards.

While resting at Nicopolis by the side of the placid gulf, Paul reviewed to Luke and Titus his trips through Spain and Dalmatia and told of the friends he had left there. He was worn and weary; the evening shadows from the peninsula on which they were, creeping away from them across the bay to the farther shore, seemed to him as if they were a curtain, softly, slowly drawing over his years of activity. Now he was compelled to rest; the days of unflagging zeal were gone forever. As the sheen of the gulf lost the glint of the sun and mirrored up the distant stars, so he, while losing the fierce energy of his early life, was reflecting back to the heavens the glory of his faith.

"Titus, you must leave at once for Dalmatia," said Paul. "For they need help. They have written me of their troubles."

After Titus left, Paul and Luke spent days in reviewing Paul's life and their experiences since they had become companions in spreading the glad tidings.

Then came the soldiers, who arrested Paul and hurried him off to Rome. Luke went with him, at great peril, as he was told by the guards. While Paul and Luke had heard of the persecution and had met many who were fugitives, they understood that the brutal saturnalia had passed. So by ship to Brundisium and then on horseback to Rome, the guards hurried their prisoner forward; yet Paul had won their confidence.

In Rome a crowd of men and women were being examined, who had been arrested in the raid led by Alexander. Women were in tears. Men were in anguish, but sternly awaited their fate. Helius was dressed as a military officer and had with him two citizens of counsel.

"We will put the test question first," said Helius to his associates, who nodded assent.

"All who will renounce any allegiance to this sect step to the front and take the oath," said Helius, addressing the crowd of prisoners.

Alexander, who had been arrested with them when acting as a spy, was the only one who stepped to the front and placed himself in posture for the oath.

The rest of the prisoners looked on Alexander in scorn. An old, patriarchal man beckoned for permission to speak, which being given, he said in a loud voice:

"We do not know this man. He is not and has never been one of us."

Alexander in fear stepped behind the guards. The judges looked admiringly on the group of twenty or more men and women.

"The people are sick of spectacles," said Helius to his associates. "In Nero's absence, we will mercifully sentence them to death."

The associates silently acquiesced, and Helius simply said to the lictors, as a matter of form:

"The sentence is death."

Helius was talking lightly with his associates while the guards were driving and leading the condemned out and Alexander approached, sycophantly bowing to Helius.

"What news have you about the arrest of Paul?" Alexander asked. "I have done all that was required of me."

"As soon as the officers arrive with him, we will have the preliminary hearing," Helius said, impatiently. "We have just condemned many of your race to death, and still you persist."

"They were only incidental to the capture of Paul, a condition which you imposed," said Alexander.

"A middle-aged man, with hate centuries old," said Helius to his associates, as Alexander left.

Paul had bravely insisted that he would ride at the pace set by the guards, from Brundisium, although he was worn and almost fainting. Luke interposed on behalf of the aged prisoner. Paul kindly urged that he would bear the long and arduous trip from Brundisium to Rome, if need be, without rest; but the officer in charge stopped at different inns on the way so as to give the apostle an opportunity to rest. They entered the praetorium while the prisoners condemned by Helius were being led, as they believed, to await their execution, followed by a crowd of curious men and women. Paul aroused and gave them the sign of blessing, which caused them to recognize and call to him, although the guards brutally beat them back into the line.

Luke supported Paul into the corridor of the prison, and, after gently laying him down on a bench, bathed Paul's head from a basin of water furnished by the guards.

"Go and tell our friends that I am here, and may have a chance to speak to them," said Paul to Luke, after being revived by Luke's ministrations.

While Paul was being cared for by Luke in the prison, a meeting was being held by six of the leaders of the Christians, both Jews and Greeks; and Demas, who had stood high in the esteem of Paul, was the spokesman.

"The persecutions are being renewed, and leaders are now sought. Already they have arrested Peter and given him a preliminary hearing," said Demas. "We can now make our escape."

The leaders were astonished at that instant by the entry of Luke. He told them of Paul's arrest, that the beloved teacher wanted to see them and counsel with them. He noticed that they had on their heavy coats and had their packs with them, and he looked at them questioningly.

"Yes, we are making our escape," said Demas. "We can do Paul no good, and if we remain, we only sacrifice our lives to no purpose."

Luke upbraided them for their cowardice and reminded them that Paul had given his life to the cause, without thought of himself or of danger.

"We may live to teach in our own country," said Demas. "But if we remain, we die unknown. Give our love to Paul, but we go to our own cities."

When Luke returned to Paul, the guard was kneeling beside him.

"Never fear for your soul," said Paul, laying his hand on the shoulder of the guard, "for you must perform your duty; and if I lose my life, I can suffer no more than I have suffered."

Luke reported all that he had learned and Paul told Luke to insist on a hearing as soon as possible. It was then late in the evening and Luke made Paul as comfortable as he could for the night.

"I will be on duty during the night," said the new guard to Luke as he left. "I will gladly give him aid, for I am his friend."

In his fevered sleep that night Paul had a vision of an angelic visitor. The moonlight was streaming through the window on his face, now showing the deep lines of care and hardship. The guard was standing close by, looking down on him in pity. Paul feebly raised his hands and said softly:

"I come quickly."

The guard watched closely, and often during the night paused to admire the sleeping figure whose face, even in repose, expressed the confidence and courage of one who had faith beyond the power of man to destroy. The guard at daybreak furtively brought Paul a bowl of steaming food, which refreshed and strengthened him.

I COME QUICKLY

In the early morning the guards and Luke assisted Paul to the hall of hearing before Helius. The civilian counselors were present, and Alexander stood near the table, eager to give his statements. A guard provided a chair for Paul, an act that caused Helius to study the prisoner closely. Helius grudgingly told Alexander to make his statement.

Alexander licked his lips, as if he were about to enjoy a choicest morsel, and proceeded with his charge in a wandering way, his recital covering all the accusations that had been made against Paul in Philippi, Corinth, and Jerusalem in the years past, mingling charges of violating the Jewish law with charges that he taught men against the Roman government. In his mad zeal he turned to denounce Paul to his face.

"This man is a falsifier," said Paul, rising and looking Alexander in the eye until he quailed. "He is merely a fanatical enemy who has pursued me for years, a coppersmith, and a Jew who profits by making images for idol worshipers, while he believes idols to be condemned by God."

Alexander, feeling that Paul had given him a hard thrust, and might slip away from the charges, became vehement in a rehearsal of his former statements.

"Stop," cried Helius to Alexander. "If you continue your accusations, we will be compelled to release him. We will submit the question to Nero, now in Corinth."

A messenger was dispatched, with a statement of the case, to Nero.

Onesiphorus, formerly of Iconium, now of Ephesus, had journeyed to Rome in an effort to enlarge his trade, and heard the rumor that Paul had been arrested.

Notwithstanding Christians pointed out the great danger he ran if he sought Paul, he visited Paul in prison and with Luke ministered to his comfort. The fearlessness of Onesiphorus encouraged others less courageous and a way was always found to permit visitors to see Paul.

Paul, in his longing for old friends and those whom he dearly loved, had Luke write to Timothy to hasten to him before the winter would close the seas. He learned of the friends who had been slaughtered in the wild days of the persecution following the fire, and gave all those who visited him encouragement in their sorrows. They bewailed the fate that awaited him, and he replied:

"As once I wrote to you, so I repeat, with the sword poised over my head:

"'I am persuaded, that neither death, nor life, nor angels, nor principalities, nor things present, nor things to come, nor powers, nor height, nor depth, nor any other creation, shall be able to separate us from the love of God, the love which is in Christ Jesus our Lord.'"

CHAPTER XLII

BY THE OSTIAN WAY

The scheming Tigellinus spent his time close to Nero in Corinth and pretended an interest in the silly efforts of Nero, attempting in his inordinate egotism to be a leader in the games and in the revival of music, dancing, and histrionic art. Sabinus came with the messenger asking for advice as to the disposition of prominent Christians being held for final hearing. He intended to return, if the answer was favorable to release; and if Nero would show no mercy, then he had decided that he would remain in Corinth and let Helius dispose of the disagreeable situation. Nero, at the time Sabinus and the messenger arrived, was in the midst of training a chorus of dancing girls. Several Roman flatterers were in attendance, as well as Tigellinus, watching that no one caught the vagrant fancy of Nero.

Nero stopped his dancers; and, going down from his director's chair, representing a throne, went through ludicrous contortions with his fat body to show the chorus—twenty girls in filmy garments—how to dance gracefully. The instant his back was turned, they were laughing while the courtiers praised him.

"It is well," said Nero to Sabinus, while panting from his exertions, "that I can train this generation in the lost art of grace."

"We have a mob of deluded Christian followers and many of the leaders of the Christian sect under arrest in Rome," said Sabinus, "to serve for a spectacle; but the people rudely cry for the emperor to be served, instead of these victims, who make no resistance. The people almost fall down in worship of them."

"Here I am wearing myself away," said Nero, "to give my people the poetry of motion, and they do not appreciate it. Who are the men?"

"There are many you do not know of," said Sabinus, "but we have the two principals, Peter and Paul."

"I have heard of Peter," said Nero, swelling with anger, "and Paul, Paul, a rank mountebank. He persuaded my beautiful Lalagen to quit the bower I had fitted up for her and serve among the common women, in his organization." Turning to an attendant, he said, "Write a rescript to Rome, ordering the death of these two men, unless they recant; and to release all the rest. That will show the people that I pursue the consistent course of a statesman."

Meanwhile, during the early winter months, the friends of Paul had gathered from the four corners of the globe, defying the dangers that beset them. Timothy came at once, with John Mark. The guards were oppressed with visitors. The common people who had not believed the Christian teachings were growing louder in their mutterings, and were eager to learn the story of Paul. They stood in open places, hailing his visitors, to learn more of the man. He was rapidly becoming a hero in the eyes of the uncertain mob. Helius delayed action, because he feared the political results, and wrote to Sabinus. He received a second rescript from Nero, to proceed as formerly directed.

It was in the balmy days of June, 67 A.D., that Helius had Paul brought before him. Felix and Alexander, under notice, were present. Notwithstanding great caution had been used to avoid publicity, a large crowd followed the guards up to the steps leading to the trial chamber. The case against Peter had been disposed of; and now Paul was the last to be heard, if the proceedings could be called a hearing.

Helius had several civilians for counsel, but all were time-servers of the emperor, present only to give an air of judicial consideration to the proceeding. Felix and Alexander were there, although Felix adroitly refused to converse with the Jew; and, noticing the contempt that Helius had for Alexander, Felix turned his back to him. When the case was called, Alexander stepped to the front and started to talk.

"This business is bad enough, without having to listen to you," said Helius.

The special guard ordered by Helius was in charge of Longinus, who, recognizing Paul, almost forgot his dignity as a centurion.

"This is the second rescript in this case," said Helius, unrolling a manuscript. "The emperor has magnanimously, out of the tenderness of his poetical nature, ordered the release of the followers of this sect who were arrested about the time these charges were preferred; but, with that firmness found in a wise ruler, he demands that we apply the test in this case of Paul, as formerly it has been applied. Let the prisoner stand forth."

Paul stood up, with a guard who strangely pressed close to him.

"Will you under oath renounce this name you teach?" said Helius.

The guard whispered in Paul's ear:

"Take the oath. Many have taken it. It means nothing, because extorted by threats."

Paul did not indicate that he heard the guard, but answered reverently:

"For me to live is Christ, and to die is gain."

The counselors of Helius plainly showed their admiration of the courage of the apostle.

"There is no discretion left us," said Helius. "Under this rescript you must die. Being a Jew, you will be crucified."

Paul stepped forward, aroused to his most sublime attitude, the weight of years falling away as he straightened up before the Roman court and said:

"Because of one immortalized Crucifixion in Jerusalem, which I would not suffer to be imitated on my humble person, and because I am a Roman citizen, I demand that my death be at the block."

After a conference with his counselors, Helius said:

"Be it so."

The soldiers, under Longinus, led the way, clearing the steps by pushing back the crowds, followed by the guards in charge of Paul.

"Nero's lions were not hungry," said a loud-voiced brawler on the edge of the crowd, "and now he kills off the men who think of us."

This brought such a cheer from the crowd that the guards faced on each side toward the crowd, with spears at charge; and the miserable plebeians fell back.

Ten days passed, the time required by law between the sentence and death, during which the friends assembled daily in the streets near the praetorium, that

Paul might know they loved him. The word had passed quickly that the other worshipers had been released and only the two leaders had been held. So great was the throng of visitors to the distinguished condemned that guards almost feared an uprising.

In the very early morning of the fateful day, Longinus came with his escort to lead Paul to a secluded place of execution, the Acque Salvie, 2 miles south of the Ostian gate, a hollow, level space, surrounded by hills. Even at that early hour, Paul's friends, who had spent the night in watching and praying, accompanied the procession in great numbers, followed by a rabble that delighted in blood.

Helius felt it necessary to attest by eye-witnesses that the sentence had been carried out; and he caused to be erected a canopy and a platform, furnished with comfortable chairs, on the side of a hill, in full view of the place of execution, where he assembled fifty nobles and senators. Felix was among the invited guests. Alexander came crowding in among them and, by order of Helius, was ignominiously kicked out.

The beheading block was at the center of a space marked off by posts on the low level ground, and soldiers on guard prevented any unauthorized person from entering the segregated area. The professional executioner, leaning on his massive sword, awaited the preparations. Longinus led Paul to the block and with tears in his eyes took Paul's hand to bid him farewell.

"Grieve not, nor condemn yourself," said Paul, "for you only obey a government that you serve."

An assistant of the executioner stepped forward to bind Paul and to blindfold him. Paul protested to

Longinus that he would submit, without being bound or blindfolded, but would crave the favor of saying a last word to the group of weeping friends, who stood as near as the guards would permit.

The request was granted. While Paul spoke, Timothy, recognizing that the words were from the letter to him, lifted his face toward heaven in silent prayer. The rest of the friends ceased weeping; their faces lighted up with the glory of their faith. A solemn stillness fell on all, while Paul spoke in ecstatic tones:

> "I have fought a good fight;
> I have finished the course,
> I have kept the faith;
> Henceforth there is laid up for me the crown of
> righteousness,
> Which the Lord, the righteous judge, shall give
> to me at that day;
> And not to me only,
> But also to all them that have loved his appear-
> ing."

Kneeling, he laid his head on the grooved block. The assembled Christians held their breath. The idlers bowed their heads. Helius and his friends, though inured to brutal scenes, were so touched by the fearlessness of the man that they turned their eyes away.

The executioner swung his sword.

Longinus gave Paul's friends permission to take away the body. While they reverently placed the remains on a stretcher, Longinus and his guards, without any command, formed in open column for the mourners to pass through, as if it were a funeral of state.

Helius and his friends slipped away.

Luke, Timothy, Titus, and Mark, followed by the silent mourners, daring death by their presence, gently bore the martyred chieftain to an unmarked place of burial by the Ostian Way. They believed that his name and work would be revered and hallowed by his "joint heirs," long after any memorial of granite would be destroyed by the elements.

INDEX

INDEX

6154 6 4 3